Shell
Treasury of the
Countryside

EDITED BY
JOHN BAKER

AND WITH
CONTRIBUTIONS BY

WALTER SHEPHERD KENNETH LINDLEY
RALPH WHITLOCK EDWARD PYDDOKE
IAN CORNWALL RICHARD FITTER
G H COOK

WITH 140 PICTURES IN
MONOCHROME AND COLOUR

Phoenix House · London

© Text, Shell-Mex and BP Ltd, 1965
Illustrations as acknowledged
Set by
The Aldine Press · Letchworth · Herts
and printed by
Latimer, Trend & Co. Ltd · Whitstable · Kent
for
J. M. DENT & SONS LTD
Aldine House · Bedford Street • London
A Phoenix House publication
First published 1965

The pictures used in Chapter 8 are from *The Shell Nature Book* and are by Edith and Rowland Hilder, p. 70, p. 72 (Teazle). S. R. Badmin, R.W.S., p. 71. Maurice Wilson and Rowland Hilder, p. 74 (Blue-tit), p. 76 (Goldfinch), p. 78, p. 79, p. 80 (Chaffinch). John Leigh-Pemberton, p. 74 (A stoat), p. 75, p. 76 (Lapwing), p. 77, p. 80 (Yellow wagtail) (Yellowhammer).

Acknowledgments

THE thanks of the publishers and editor are due to the following for permission to reproduce the illustrations as under:

G. P. Abraham, p. 9, p. 12, p. 13; George Allen (Ashmolean Museum), p. 37; T. P. Backhouse, p. 60 (An astonishing brick church); John Baker, p. 19 (Piggle Dene), p. 36, p. 40 (Length and lock), p. 43 (Snow fences), p. 51 (Thatch on roofs) (A deer on the thatch), p. 73 (Rosebay willowherb); G. H. Cook, p. 67; Crown Copyright (British Regional Geology), p. 16; Crown Copyright (Geological Museum), p. 8, p. 11 (Terraces or shelves); *The Field*, p. 88 (Wessex Saddleback pig), p. 90; Marjorie Howard, p. 24; Lawrence Jones, p. 57 (Garden, church and thatch), p. 60 (A soaring stone tower), p. 61 (Towers) (Timber spires); John Laing, p. 45; Kenneth Lindley, p. 5, p. 23, p. 33, p. 35, p. 40 (Aqueduct), p. 47 (Blenheim Palace), p. 53 (Brick, flint and elegance) (Butcher), p. 56 (Tombstone), p. 60 (Elegance in stone) (A lantern of light); London and Wide World Photos, p. 87 (Scottish blackface sheep), p. 88 (Landrace pigs); I. D. Margary, p. 34 (Roman braking system); Massey-Ferguson, p. 89 (Tractors); Nicholas Meyjes, p. 84 (Friesian cow) (Dairy Shorthorn cow), p. 85 (Hereford bull), p. 86 (Jersey cow), p. 87 (Galloway cow and calf), p. 88 (Romney Marsh ram); National Buildings Record, p. 39, p. 47 (Warwick Castle), p. 48 (Cruck cottage), p. 49, p. 51 ('Black and white' house) (Flint and brick), p. 52 (Brick and tile) (Pargeting) (Weatherboarded cottages), p. 53 (Georgian period), p. 55 (Market crosses), p. 56 (Corn Exchange), p. 59 (Crosses before churches) (Rough and solid) (A stave church), p. 63 (Gargoyles) (A font in each church) (Scratch or Mass dial), p. 65 (Graffiti); Alfred Proctor, p. 44 (Saltash Bridge), p. 57 (River, church and castle, p. 58 (Church and manor); Pictorial Colour Slides, p. 22 (Viking ship) p. 26 (Stonehenge), p. 27 (Avebury) (Axe and dagger) (Tools), p. 29 (The Long Man of Wilmington), p. 44 (Menai bridge), p. 47 (Richmond Castle), p. 53 (Chemist); W. W. Roberts, p. 69 (Spring scene) (Beech in spring) (Giant oak) (Lombardy poplar) (Elm), p. 72 (Oxford ragwort) (Ragged robin) (Cuckoo pint), p. 73 (Bee orchid); Society of Antiquaries, p. 28 (A fallen defender); Walter Shepherd, p. 9 (The V underlies the U), p. 10, p. 11 (An ox-bow lake), p. 14, p. 15, p. 17; A. C. Smith (*Antiquities of North Wiltshire*), p. 19 (The Devil's Den), p. 25, p. 27 (Potsherds or shards); Sport and General, p. 85 (Aberdeen Angus steer); J. K. St Joseph, p. 20, p. 28 (Maiden Castle), p. 29 (Oldest White Horse), p. 30 (Seeing into the ground) (Square Celtic fields), p. 31, p. 34 (Roman roads), p. 41, p. 46, p. 47 (Gardens of the big house), p. 48 (A 'lost' village); E. B. Talbot, p. 58 (Guild carvings) (Minstrels), p. 61 (Kinds of roofs) (Stonemasons); Tierpark, Munich, p. 84 (The auroch); L. F. Thompson, p. 86 (Highland cattle), p. 87 (Hampshire Down lambs), p. 89 (Suffolk mare and foals).

Contents

1: Introduction—
Man Moulds the
Countryside

THE face of Britain is alive with treasures of the past and the present. Merely to journey across it is exciting. Every turn of the road, every field, every copse, has a tale to tell. The purpose of this little book is to encourage its readers to investigate some of these remarkable things, to make every journey a tour of discovery.

For more than a hundred thousand years man has been making and leaving behind him his *artifacts*. It's a good word, though you won't find it in every dictionary. It means anything made by man, from a castle to a coin. This book is, in the main, concerned with man-made things in the country.

Of all the artifacts in England, perhaps even in Europe, Stonehenge is the most remarkable. Erected over three thousand years ago its purpose is still mysterious. For most of its time it stood as a silent relic of the immense past. All kinds of legends grew around it, mostly fairy stories about the Druids and others. It suffered the plunderings of builders and spoilers. They fancied not only the native sarsen stone for their walls, cottages and barns but the blue stones which, a mystery in themselves, had somehow been brought from Wales.

In our own time we take care of this treasure of Salisbury Plain.

Ten years ago an incident occurred which threw a sudden light on the people who built it. A schoolboy discovered engravings of an axe and a dagger on one of the great upright stones; and you can see them plainly next time you go there. These weapons were known to be of Greek type, and they showed vividly that our ancestors were not isolated barbarians but had dealings with the high Mediterranean civilizations. (There is also the curious matter of the blue faience beads from Egypt, found in British graves thousands of years old, but that's another story.)

There are lessons in this tale. First, that we must treasure our treasures. Had we not learned to respect Stonehenge in an age when we could easily have destroyed it this world - famous monument would merely be a legend. Second, that, since writing did not exist in England before the Romans, anything before their arrival must be given special care and special study. Third, that our forefathers were not to be despised as woad-covered savages simply because they lived five thousand years ago and hadn't passed their 11-plus. Fourth, that the sharp eyes of a reader of this book might prove as valuable as the learning of scholars.

.   .   .

5

So man is an inveterate maker. He cannot stop making things. He makes many things which outlast him—and it is surprising what fragile things (woven cloth, for example) do that. In this book we describe man-made things in the open air. Here are chapters on landscape and scenery, on the Ancient Britons and their visible works, on ways, tracks and roads, on hedges and fields, on farming and farm animals, on birds and beasts, on villages and country towns, on churches and castles—on the thousand things to be noticed on any journey. To see them you will have to use the by-roads and the footpaths. (In 1944 an Act of Parliament was passed and maps were made fixing footpaths and bridle-ways for all time.) And you'll have to be out in the winter as well as the summer. It's another, and quite as interesting, England; and you get better viewing when the leaves are off the trees.

You may be surprised to read of man 'making' birds and animals, but he does. He has certainly altered the landscape. Much of what we think of as natural scenery is man-made, from his 2,000-year-old Celtic fields, still to be faintly seen, to his modern fields of huge size growing miles of wheat, oats and barley. Even the grass, as we see it, and many of the trees, are man-made or man-introduced. The tall poplar comes from France and the horse chestnut from the Balkans. Certainly man has made and altered waterways and lakes, and (at Silbury) has even built a considerable hill. So that the chapters of this book dealing with 'wild' things, with birds, animals and flowers, are also chapters dealing with man's artifacts.

By the pressure of man old species have been reduced or driven out but new species have been introduced. We all know how the rabbits have been nearly killed off and that cornfields do not shine with red poppies as they used to; that many weeds and wild flowers called 'common' in the manuals are getting quite uncommon. But we should notice, too, that hares are more to be seen and that the brave poppy has adapted itself to the verges of the new trunk roads. If partridges grow scarce, the asiatic pheasant, a real foreigner, struts cheekily about. If the prickly teazle is harder to find, the pink cones of the fireweed are like an invasion. Many wild flowers are escapers from man's gardens. They have taken to the fields with enthusiasm: evening primrose is one in Surrey.

And man, of course, has changed, by breeding, the shape of cows and bulls and sheep and pigs. Their ancestors would hardly know them.

We talked earlier of the difference between casually looking and really seeing. Kenneth Lindley explains this difference in our third chapter. It is astonishing how you can train your eyes, detective-like, to note things which most people ignore. Not necessarily tiny things, but big and obvious things. There is the story of the man who noted the simple fact that in many fields cows were inclined to push their heads

6

through the field wire and eat the grass on road verges. How odd! But this simple observation, in the end, led to an investigation which showed that the verge grass contained valuable minerals which the cows needed, and to a world-wide study of grass pastures. Think too of the famous Mr Hosier. He lived in a Wiltshire village and wondered, rather simply perhaps, why farmers continued, as they had done for centuries, to go through the tricky business of driving cows from miles away, through mud and muck, to farm buildings for milking. Why not take the milking shed to the cows? So he invented the milking bale, which now trundles around everywhere following the cows. And the cows, with gratitude, now queue up for milking as soon as the bale appears.

Seeing is one thing, but to *understand* you must also *look for something* and try to see the pattern in which we all live. We give you clues in this book to the remarkable (but by no means always the rare) and the lovely things to be seen in this pattern, as the background of our lives.

We have talked of man's artifacts and his victory over his circumstances. Man has come a long way since his ancestors dwelt in pits on bleak hill tops, but his victory cannot be complete. Every time you turn on a tap you are using a natural product which has its beginnings in broad acres of the country under a rainy sky; every time you eat you consume something grown in a field.

There has to be a moral of course. Britain has many wonders and beauties in every square mile. This is a book of wonders, natural and man-made. But, in looking and wondering, remember this: we did not make these things—they come to us from all our yesterdays. We have therefore no right to spoil or destroy them. And we upset nature at our peril if we break the pattern. Every thread is interlocked.

2: The Making of Landscape

HAVE you ever wondered why some mountain you have seen has such a curious shape? It may look like a cone, a top-hat, an upturned basin or a flight of steps, and there may be more than one reason why it does so. But of this you can be pretty sure—it is a piece of sculpture; nothing less. It has not, of course, been shaped by human hands, but it has been carved all the same—a bit chipped off here, a rough edge sandpapered down there, a hollow gouged out in another place, and perhaps a knob sharpened to a point on top, or cut to look like a horn, or a mushroom, or a castle battlement. These queer effects are the work of several different sculptors. Frost is the chief chipper, wind and rain are the chief smoothers, water, snow and ice are the chief gougers, and the ornaments owe their unexpected shapes to the rock itself, which is hard in some places but soft in others.

These sculptors work by stealth, for you hardly ever see them actually *doing* anything, but you can generally tell which of them is guilty if you look carefully around

V-shaped valley at Ramsden Clough, Yorks.

U-shaped valley in the Pass of Llanberis, Caernarvonshire

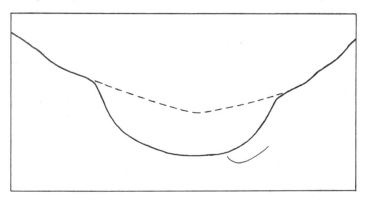

The V underlies the U, as this diagram shows

for clues. You can often solve the mystery without even leaving your seat at a picnic, or while driving slowly along in a car.

You must, of course, learn a few of the detective's tricks if you are to become adept at it. For example, to understand mountains you must pretend to look the other way and gaze at the valleys between them instead, for the sides of the mountains are also the sides of the valleys, and only the valleys can show what has been cut away by the carvers. The mountains show what has been left. If a valley is shaped like a huge V, it has always belonged to a river and the mountains

9

on either side of it were carved by water. If it is shaped like a U, it was made by a glacier during the Great Ice Age and the mountains were carved by ice. There are plenty of good examples of both kinds in the mountainous parts of the country, and two are illustrated here.

The picture of the Pass of Llanberis is particularly interesting because, if you look carefully, you will see that the upper slopes of the valley are much less steep, and they would, if continued in their downward directions, meet in the middle to make a wide, flat V. They are all that is left of a much older river valley, which flowed at a higher level until the glacier came and scooped out its deep U right down the centre. (See the diagram.)

The very tops of the mountains have forms which depend partly on their age and partly on the rocks they are made of. Generally speaking, smooth rounded tops, like pillows, mean that the mountains are very old, and that the weather has been at work on them for millions of years. Unlike human beings, mountains grow shorter as they get older, and very high rugged mountains are either young ones or made of very hard rock indeed.

Bare, jagged peaks like spires and ruined castles are of hard rock which has been split and chipped by frost, for nothing else can touch them. Their natural cracks get filled with rain-water which freezes at night, and pieces of the rock then burst off for the same reason that water-pipes burst in very cold weather. The cracks get sealed up

Meanders showing speed of water

with ice near the surface first, and then the deeper water expands as it freezes, forcing the rock apart with a pressure of about one ton per square inch. At the foot of every crag you will see a huge pile— called a 'scree'—of the pieces which have been split off during its carving.

Looking into the valley again you may notice lots of interesting things from the rivers flowing in them. Because a river tends to wind about, travelling from side to side as well as flowing down, it gradually widens the bottom of its valley. It brings down mud, sand and gravel and presently carpets the floor of the valley with a flat 'flood-plain', which is often occupied by water-meadows. This we have often been 'told', but it is much more interesting to see with our own eyes how it comes about.

You may find the vital clues wherever a stream or river flows round a fairly sharp curve. Here you will spot at once that the inside of the curve has a flat shore with perhaps a little beach, and the water is shallow, whereas the outside of the curve has a steep bank with perhaps a cliff or 'bluff', and the water is deep. If you watch a floating leaf you will also notice that the water on the inside of the curve is moving very slowly, while that on the outside is moving swiftly.

This may remind you of a company of soldiers on the march. At the order, 'Right—wheel!' the file on the inside of the curve slows down, or even marks time, while the file on the outside has to 'step out lively' in order to get round without getting out of line. The drawing shows how this applies to a river, the lengths of the arrows representing the speed of the water.

Now, where the water is sweeping round the outside of the curve it is scouring away the bank and undermining it, and at the same time it is hustling along all the loose stones on the river-bed and so making it deeper. But on the inside, where it has slowed down, the opposite is happening. It drops most of the mud it was carrying, for mud settles in still water, and the sand and stones it was sweeping along its bed come to a halt and build up a beach.

An ox-bow lake. The river winds until it meets itself

The result of building up a beach on one side, and removing the bank on the other, is that the river moves sideways across its valley, and if you give it enough time it will gradually lay a carpet of sand and stones several miles wide, even though the stream itself is no bigger than a road. This explains how little rivers often have wide flat valleys, but there is another curious thing you can observe too.

Once a river has started to flow in even a slight curve, the events just described steadily increase the curve until presently it makes a wide semicircle. But it does not stop there. The semicircle becomes

Terraces or shelves showing old valley floors on the River Findhorn, Inverness-shire

three-quarters of a circle and, finally, the ends join to make a complete loop with an island in the middle. The river now by-passes the loop, which forms what is called an 'ox-bow lake'. It is by no means uncommon for rivers to come round and meet themselves in this way, and you may find plenty of examples like the one in the drawing, even in streams not much bigger than ditches.

These things you may see from the windows of a car or a train while travelling through a valley, and you may also notice—if you look farther away—one or more curious ledges running along the sides of the valley like shelves. They are called 'terraces' and look artificial, but they too are the work of the river and tell something of its past history. They are the remains of the river's old flood-plains, when it was flowing along higher levels. What happened was that, after the river had made itself a nice wide flood-plain, the land began to rise or tilt up. This is happening in many places today, only the movement is so slow—perhaps a quarter of an inch in twenty years—that nobody notices it. But its effect on the river is to give it a steeper slope and make it flow faster, so it starts cutting itself a new valley in the middle of its old flood-plain. It may do this several times, with intervals of rest between, as you can see in this picture of the River Findhorn. Here there are at least three terraces, all of them formed during the last ten thousand years or so.

When a river enters a lake its waters are brought nearly to a standstill, and by checking it in this way the lake signs its own death-warrant. It is really the old story of

A lake being infilled at Derwentwater, Cumberland

12

A lake infilled at Borrowdale, Cumberland

building up a beach again, for the stones and pebbles now stop rolling along, and the sand and mud—there is often a great deal of mud—settle down on the bottom. Thus the river gradually fills the lake up. The picture of Lake Derwentwater shows this in visible progress, and you can see it happening yourself even in a very small pond if a stream flows into it. The lake will eventually become entirely filled and will no doubt support fields and farms, as has happened at Borrow- dale in the next picture.

Look at the picture of Borrowdale again. You may suspect that the rough, knobbly tops of the mountains must be of some hard volcanic rock, but though in this case you would be right, the only way to be sure is to go and look at them. In other districts hard sandstones and limestones may crown a mountain with bare rock, so you cannot

always tell from a distance. Sometimes, however, there are parallel beds of rock and the mountain is like a layer-cake, and then you may see how the ends of the beds have been cut off short by the carvers, making an inland cliff or 'escarpment'.

In many districts you can tell the kind of rock which forms the landscape from the colour of the soil in ploughed fields, or even by the varieties of wild plants which grow by the roadside. There is no mistaking the rich red soils overlying the New Red Sandstone in parts of the west and centre of England, for example, or the light grey soils of the chalk country in the east and south. Among the plants there are many common species which flourish over sandstone but fail to thrive on limestone, and vice versa, and others which demand the water-holding properties of clay or shale.

Heather, gorse, bracken, foxglove, pine and sweet chestnut grow on lime-free soils rich in silica, and these are found over sandstones, granite and flint gravels. The appearance of rhododendrons in gardens at the foot of the Downs shows infallibly where the chalk ends, because lime is poison to these plants. On the other hand, scabious, bee orchis, viper's bugloss, valerian, dogwood, wild cherry and deadly nightshade are found only where there is abundant limestone. Most stone fruits, and members of the cabbage family, must also have lime, but this may be supplied by the farmers, and artificially grown crops are a less useful guide than the wild plants.

No large trees grow on pure chalk, so that a clump of trees on the top of a chalk hill is a sure sign that the hill is capped with 'clay-with-flints', and the chances are that the trees are beeches. Oaks and willows prefer lowland clay soils, and the grey foliage of a line of willows marking the course of a stream is often recognizable from a great distance. Rushes and bog-plants also need water and in flat land grow over true clay formations, or in clays brought down by rivers, but they also grow in the clay which accumulates in hollows on mountains of igneous rocks.

Another way to tell the rocks of a district is from the older buildings in it. Before the age of mechanized transport houses were built of the nearest suitable material, and so we find buildings of sandstone, limestone, slate or granite according to

An escarpment showing strata of rocks

the local rock. Old timber buildings indicate former oak forests growing on clay, bricks show that clay is not far off, and flint buildings mean that we are in the chalk country. Aberdeen is called the 'granite city' for a similar reason. Unusual stone roofs, such as those made of thick slabs of Horsham stone or Bath stone, are sure signs of quarries at no great distance, but roofing slates are no guide because they have been transported from North Wales all over the country since the reign of Elizabeth I.

Walls separating fields are particularly useful, for their stones were often picked or quarried from those same fields. They will show, for example, when you have crossed the boundary between the Carboniferous limestone and the Millstone grit. In Norway a local geological survey was conducted by observing the distribution of disease in cattle—a very cunning piece of detective work. Animals grazing in pasture over rocks containing phosphorus were healthy, while those in adjoining pastures · betrayed the boundary of these rocks by suffering from a bone disease due to phosphorus deficiency.

If you are especially interested in

rocks the most rewarding places to visit are the cliffs at the seaside, and there are also river-cliffs, quarries and chalk-pits. All sorts of rock formations may be seen in cliffs, and unless you are in a district like Land's End, where the rocks are of granite or volcanic in origin, you seldom have to explore far to see a good example of 'bedding'.

1 A tailed Trilobite, found in the older rocks of Wales and the border counties. It flourished on the sea-floor about 400 million years ago, and its whole race is extinct. This specimen came from Wenlock, in Shropshire.

2 An Ammonite from Whitby, in Yorkshire, where it is called a 'St Hilda's serpent' because it looks like a coiled snake. Other ammonites may be found in the Midlands and south of England, and in Kent (at Folkestone). They are common in limestones and clays, but became extinct about 150 million years ago.

3 'Lamp-shells' from moderately old rocks in the Midlands of England. Though they look like ordinary sea-shells or Molluscs, they really belong to a totally different kind of creature and are called Brachiopods. Most of them are extinct.

4 This is an extinct relative of the oyster, and its folk-name is 'Devil's toenail'. It is found in clays in Dorset, Gloucestershire and the Midlands. It lived about 170 million years ago.

5 An extinct relative of the scallop. It comes from a sandstone in Cambridgeshire, where it lived about 120 million years ago. Fossils of sea-shells of all kinds are common in a great many rocks in the Midlands, south and east of England.

6 A fossil sea-urchin from the chalk hills. The folk-name for this species is 'Shepherd's crown', though it measures only about two inches across. They became extinct about 80 million years ago, but other kinds of sea-urchins live in British seas today.

7 Fossil sharks' teeth from the London Clay. The London Clay settled down in a shallow sea about 60 million years ago, when the climate of southern England was tropical.

Stack, arch, cave, at Covesea, Elgin

Most of our cliffs are of sandstone, limestone (which includes chalk), shale or clay, and all these rocks were formed from sediments deposited on the bottoms of ancient seas. They were originally laid down in level layers, and the layers are often still visible, though they have been hardened and raised above sea level for some millions of years. They are called 'beds' or 'strata', and sometimes you will see a bed of one kind of rock resting on a different kind—let us say a bed of clay or shale resting on a bed of limestone. A little detective work here may reveal several interesting secrets.

First of all, look to see if the beds of clay are parallel with the beds of limestone, and form a continuation of them. If so it means that the fairly deep water in which the limestone was formed became shallower because the sea-bed rose. This brought it within reach of the mud being brought down by rivers. If the junction is absolutely sudden there *could* have been a catastrophic arrival of enormous quantities of mud as the result of an earthquake or a landslide, and that something of this sort happened in what is

now Dorsetshire at least 100 million years ago is told by the fossils in the rocks.

The bed of limestone here was laid down in clear water and supported thousands of acres of sealilies. Their fossils appear right through the limestone, but just the heads of the top layer are in the clay. The clay begins quite suddenly and it evidently arrived quickly enough to choke and kill the sealilies while they were still standing upright, and the whole population was suddenly exterminated.

It is not often that an ancient tragedy is recorded so perfectly, but your detective work will very likely reveal an event of quite a different kind. It may happen that the beds of limestone are tilted at an angle, or even bent or 'folded' into curves, yet the clay on top is quite level. It looks as if the distorted limestone beds had been neatly sliced off with a knife, and then the clay laid down on the flat surface. Well, in such a case this is exactly what *did* happen, only the slicing was not done with a knife but by some of our old friends, the sculptors.

16

The beds of the limestone must once have been folded and raised up to form dry land, and this was worn down flat by rivers and the weather. When it sank beneath the sea again, the encroaching waves put the finishing touches to it, and then the clay was laid on top. So what you have discovered is a fossil country! The photograph shows an example of a limestone resting 'unconformably' on tilted flagstones in Yorkshire, the junction being the surface of the land about 300 million years ago.

The sea itself is the greatest of all demolition agents, for wherever it gets a chance it razes everything to the ground and batters it to fragments. It works chiefly between high and low tide-marks, where it attacks the cliff in the manner of a woodman felling a tree, hacking away at the base until it topples over. This undermining is generally visible as a 'nick' in the foot of the cliff, and where the rocks are especially soft there may be a cave. A deep cave in a projecting headland may go right through and out the other side, making a tunnel or an arch, and if the roof of this falls the outer wall will become a 'stack', or isolated pillar of rock standing out of the sea. The picture shows three of these forms all within a few yards of one another.

The materials of a beach are chiefly fragments of rock from the cliffs, but sometimes they have 'foreign' pebbles mixed with them. It is fun to look for these and try to find where they have come from.

Such pebbles have been brought along the coast from other cliffs, partly by longshore currents but most effectively by waves approaching the beach at an angle. Such waves do not merely rake the pebbles up and down the slope, but they sweep them along sideways as well. Most of the beaches on shores where there are no cliffs have arrived in this way, so that *all* their pebbles are 'foreign'.

You can see evidence of the migration of beaches at any seaside place where there are groynes, for these are built solely for the purpose of preventing the removal of the beach. You can tell which way the sea is trying to move the pebbles by comparing the height of the shingle on each side of a groyne. On one side the sea will have piled the beach up, and on the other side carried it off as far as the next groyne, as shown in the drawing.

All this is detective work, and there seems to be no end to the interesting deductions a clever observer can make if he uses his eyes. He must be a very dull person, in a very dull mood, who imagines that the stones of the seashore are of no interest except to throw at things!

Groynes prevent a beach from 'travelling'

3: To Look is not to See

EVERY reader of this book must spend the whole of his or her waking life looking at things. Looking, like breathing, is a natural function which we perform without noticing it. Looking is passive—but *seeing* is active, and this is why it appears in the title of this chapter. Once you start seeing things you really begin to wake up. Human progress largely depends on people who see things which others may have merely looked at. And seeing, making deductions from what you see.

A man recently discovered a site where metal had been worked continuously longer than anywhere else in England. He 'saw' a wall in the Forest of Dean. Thousands of people must have looked at it without really seeing it, but this man noticed that among the local stones were bits and pieces of a different colour and texture. A closer sight showed that these fragments were the slag from ancient metal-smelting processes. Further investigations revealed more and more about them, until the history of what men had done on this site over tens of centuries was revealed. You do not have to go far to make similar discoveries once you really start *seeing*.

The most important thing about seeing is to ask yourself why things are as they are. Remember that in chalk country any mark on the ground made by man can last for thousands of years! Why were buildings erected where you see them, and why were they built of certain materials and constructed in a particular way? Where did the materials come from and how did they get there? Even if building stones appear naturally in a particular place, the story of how they came to be there may be a fascinating one. There are many examples of stones appearing in places where you might not expect them, and geologists have made fascinating discoveries by inquiring how this came about.

If you travel along the Bath road, west of Marlborough in Wiltshire, you will pass a downland hollow belonging to the National Trust and called Piggle Dene. Although the downs are mostly chalk, Piggle Dene and one or two similar areas are covered with great boulders of sarsen stone, known as grey wethers because, at a distance, they looked like grazing sheep. These stones are the remains of a layer of rock which covered the chalk millions of years ago. Most of them

Piggle Dene preserved by the National Trust to show an ancient sarsen landscape, from which stones had to be removed before farming could begin

The Devil's Den, a dolmen or quoit: a prehistoric burial chamber

are scattered over the landscape, but some have been dragged into lines or circles by prehistoric men. At Clatford Bottom, a short distance from the Bath road, three stand, one across the top of the other two, to form the chamber of an ancient burial mound, called a dolmen. Later generations named this the Devil's Den, just as they named other prehistoric stones the Devil's Arrows at Boroughbridge in Yorkshire, or a natural rock formation the Devil's Chair in Shropshire. In more recent times these grey wethers were used to mark boundaries, or to guide travellers along tracks across the snow-covered hills in winter.

Stones are always worth examining, for they are the bones of the landscape. They not only provide the materials with which to build, but also shape the land itself. They hold the mystery of events far back in time, millions of years before man first appeared. The twisted layers of rock at Lulworth Cove in Dorset reveal something of the vast eruptions of the earth, an immensity

of time away, which gave us the varied splendours of our landscape. Strange imprints of sea creatures in rocks far inland, in the chalk hills, in the gravels of the Thames valley, or corals in the Derbyshire hills, are evidence of times before the seas were contained within their present boundaries. Traces of strange tropical plants in coal reveal almost unbelievable changes in climate.

You will often find heaps of stones and flints by the roadside, often gathered from stony fields. Jump out of your car and look at such heaps—you may occasionally find an artifact or a fossil. Equally look in chalk-pits for chalk fossils.

From stones you may learn to read the landscape. When man came upon the scene he began to move the stones for his own purposes. He built great monuments of natural boulders as he dug the earth into banks and ditches. He began to make his impact upon the face of the land, and he has continued to do so for thousands of years.

19

Wansdyke, a post-Roman boundary earthwork snaking its way for sixty miles through south-west England

The stone circles and avenues, and great earthen ramparts of Avebury and Stonehenge, Wiltshire, are impressive monuments of primitive man, but much remains to be discovered from less spectacular remains. Every stone, however small, can reveal something. The quarrying and shaping of stone involve considerable labour and skill, so that 'worked' stones are frequently used again when they are no longer needed for their original purpose. When the great abbeys of the Middle Ages were destroyed much of the stone was carted away for building walls, farms or cottages. Pieces of carved stone appearing unexpectedly in a village street may be all that remain of a monastery or castle. Fragments in a wall at Garendon in Leicestershire are all that can now be seen of the abbey which once occupied the site. At Salisbury the wall of the close contains much of the stone of Old Sarum, from which it was moved in the thirteenth century.

Stones of another kind can tell a very different story. Near the quay at Portmadoc in North Wales there is a shingle bank which is composed of an astonishing variety of stones. An inquiry as to how they got there will lead you, at least in imagination, to many distant parts of the world. It will involve you in the story of the growth and prosperity of the Welsh slate industry, and of the building of the harbour at Portmadoc for the ships which carried the slate away from the great quarries of Snowdonia. After unloading their heavy cargoes at distant ports these vessels took on as ballast any material which happened to be available, and so carried back to North Wales many strange and beautiful stones, which they emptied on to the shallow banks outside the harbour. These stones can reveal as much to the observer as written records do to the archivist—and surely picking up stones at the sea's edge is a more pleasant way of discovering history than reading through company records in an office or museum?

Strange stones, rusting metal, lumps of masonry, holes, pits and bumps in the ground—they each have a reason for being there. By trying to find this reason you may bring to light important facts which have been overlooked for centuries. It may be the site of a prehistoric settlement, an undiscovered battleground or a forgotten industry waiting to be discovered and inquired into. Do not make the mistake of thinking that nothing remains to be discovered in this country, merely because there are so many guide-books. Guidebooks will tell you what is already known, but this is only a fraction of

what remains to be found. Whenever the earth is disturbed, whether it is by a trowel or a bulldozer, something interesting is likely to be turned up. It might be anything from the broken stem of a clay pipe to a Roman temple; it might be a 'lost village' of which more than three hundred have quite lately been recorded! Many of the most interesting 'finds' are made by workmen or schoolboys. You might try gardening! In one morning's work the writer found (1) a loom weight, (2) a piece of medieval pot (or shard), (3) a horseshoe, (4) a flint scraper, (5) a blacksmith-made nail seven inches long.

Bumps (and holes) in the ground are always interesting. The most interesting bump of them all has puzzled men for centuries. It is known as Silbury Hill, and you pass it on the road between Marlborough and Calne. It was there when the Romans built their road, for the Roman road bends to go round it, but practically nothing else is known for certain about Silbury Hill except that it is man-made

Silbury Hill, the largest man-made mound in Europe. The Roman road to Bath at Marlborough, Wilts., curves round its base, proving its later origin

21

(excavations have proved this). Similar but smaller mounds mark the sites of many castles which have otherwise disappeared. The central tower, or 'keep', of a castle was built on a mound, known as a 'motte', for protection. Some of these, like that at Thetford, Norfolk, were immense, but many were much smaller and they stand deserted in fields, occasionally with fragments of the keep on top of them.

Banks and dykes of ancient times, though they fit naturally into the scenery, are not hard to find, nor uncommon. New ones are always being discovered, as boundary ditches, parish boundaries. The most famous of all, still quite splendid, are Wansdyke (through Gloucestershire, Wiltshire and Hampshire) and Offa's Dyke, built by the Saxons in the border country, to keep back the Welshmen!

Earth will gradually cover fallen masonry or the foundations of ruined buildings. Beside the Foss Way (now a modern motorway), near Willoughby-on-the-Wolds in Leicestershire, some mounds in the

Viking ship from Sutton Hoo, Suffolk, buried with a chieftain

fields mark the site of the Roman settlement of Vernemetum. Nothing else remains, and it is fascinating to wonder what lies beneath the surface awaiting discovery. A Viking chieftain was discovered buried with his ship and many of his treasured possessions, beneath a mound at Sutton Hoo, Suffolk. Burial mounds, like upturned pudding basins, dating from prehistoric to Saxon times are common features, singly or in groups, all over the country.

Mounds from later periods often indicate a forgotten industry. Many industries, particularly mining and quarrying, and the working of metals, produce a great deal of waste, and heaps of waste material accumulate round pits and factories. Sometimes they make a spectacular landscape feature, like the brilliant white spoil tips of the china clay workings in Devon and Cornwall, but more often they are small and inconspicuous. They are often accompanied by the ruined buildings of workshops, kilns, furnaces or mills, and a great deal of our knowledge of early industrial processes had to be gained by looking at such places. You can sometimes pick up interesting fragments of pottery and similar materials, some of them lying about on the surface, but proper excavation is a more difficult and specialized job. The digging out of the original blast furnace used by Abraham Darby at Coalbrookdale involved the removal of about fifteen thousand tons of earth and waste from the later foundries! Easier prey is the site of an old forge. There you will find piles of miscellaneous pieces of iron and you can begin guessing at what they were used for.

As you travel round the country you will discover that everything has its meaning and its own story to tell. Even the hedgerow trees and plants have more than a merely botanical interest, for many of them were introduced to this country from abroad. The animal world also has its aliens. The grey squirrel and the coypu are two, and you can even find descendants of the edible snails which the Romans imported as a delicacy. Keep looking and seeing. In this way you will begin to make your own discoveries, and to develop your own interests. If you use a camera, look for subjects worth photographing which other people do not think of taking. Every year there must be hundreds of thousands of photographs taken of the well-known cathedrals and famous 'beauty spots', and yet whole areas of our towns and villages are being pulled down to make way for new building without any record being made of the ordinary things which can be so interesting. An appeal was recently made by a local museum in a rural area for any photographs or actual examples of certain tools and articles of clothing in common use on farms in the locality until about thirty years ago, and no one was able to find any.

If you see anything which you think is particularly interesting, make a note of it. Keep a scrap album, start a home museum, try

Strata, bent and strained, at Lulworth Cove, Dorset

drawing things or, if you have a camera, take a photograph. You do not have to be a professional photographer or skilled artist to be able to do this. You will find that making notes and drawings is a very good aid to looking, as well as being a useful and interesting way of compiling your own 'guidebook' of things which the other books do not mention. Richard Jefferies once wrote that a square yard of English hedgerow contained enough to occupy a lifetime of observation. If you find anything curious or unusual, or which you cannot understand, try to find someone who can help you. Local libraries and museums are the best places to go to for help, for even if the librarian or curator cannot answer your questions he will probably be able to direct you to someone who can.

4: Tracing Ancient Britons

THE country through which we travel has been a home for man for many thousands of years. About two thousand have passed since the birth of Christ, containing the whole of our *written* history. With the Romans came the writing. All else we call prehistory.

For three thousand years before the Romans there had been farming people in our islands, occupying mainly chalk and other limestone uplands and the high moorlands of the north-west. These people of the Neolithic, or New Stone Age, our first farmers, had no metal tools and could not fell heavy timber with their stone axes. So they took to the hills, with their lighter soils and fewer trees.

Stone Age man flint-knapping

During the five or six thousand years before the arrival of the first New Stone Age farmers from the continent there had been a scattered population of hunters, fishers, fowlers and gatherers of whatever wild nature could provide, and they haunted beaches, lakesides, heaths and moorlands, wherever there was by nature fairly open country. These were the men of the Middle Stone Age. They had only temporary and seasonal settlements in such places to take advantage of whatever harvest, animal or vegetable, the country might afford at the proper times of year. They followed the food.

Still before these, back tens, and even hundreds, of thousands of years, there had been people living in Britain, at least during the more temperate intervals between the several ice advances, when the country had an almost arctic climate. They were hunters of big game — elephants, rhinoceroses, hippos and deer—and seem to have been, above all, forest and riverside dwellers, for we find their characteristic Old Stone Age tools only by water and in natural caves. Cave dwellings are still to be seen in Creswell Crags in Derbyshire and Wookey Hole in Somerset.

Neither of these peoples, the Palaeolithic (Old Stone Age) nor

24

the Mesolithic (Middle Stone Age) left traces of their occupation which can be found without digging, though many museums have collections of their stone tools, found in gravel and brick-earth pits. A rare English treasure indeed, now in the British Museum, is a piece of bone engraved with a horse's head, perhaps ten thousand years ago. It was found in Robin Hood's Cave, near Worksop in Derbyshire.

From the first farmers onwards the 'Ancient Britons' of the New Stone, the Bronze and the Early Iron Ages lived in fixed places, cleared the land, built houses, ploughed, sowed and harvested grain, mined flint, corralled their cattle and sheep, erected temples, funeral monuments and defences of wood, stone, rubble and earth. These 'Ancient Britons' have left their traces on the surface of the ground. We will now look for these.

Various barrows or prehistoric graves:
(1) long barrow, most ancient;
(2) round barrow, most common;
(3) disc barrow, less frequent

NEOLITHIC (3000–1500 B.C.)

The most striking remains of this period are the 'Long Barrows', usually near hill tops. These are communal tombs of the chiefs and are found mainly on chalk downs and limestone hills. Some are mounds of earth and chalk rubble, a hundred or more feet long and perhaps ten feet high even today. When the land has been long worked, however, they may only survive as slight rises of a couple of feet in the middle of a field. Where there is suitable stone, as in Kent, in parts of Wiltshire or in the Cotswolds, these great earthen mounds

may have covered one or more burial chambers, built of great slabs of rock, or of dry-stone walling and containing many skeletons. Sometimes the original mound has been weathered and washed away, and only the stonework remains, as in the 'dolmens' of Lanyon Quoit in Cornwall and Coldrum in Kent.

A recently excavated and restored example, with large stone structures, is the West Kennet long barrow (near Marlborough on the A 4). It is huge and you are free to walk about inside it. One which is unusually well preserved, only earth for all we know, is that just by the crossroads near Winterbourne Stoke, a mile or so beyond

Stonehenge on the Exeter road. Most of the long barrows are in Wiltshire, but there is a fair number of them (e.g. Bela's Knap, near Winchcomb, Uley and Nympsfield, both near Nailsworth, Gloucestershire) in the Cotswolds. You must really look hard for them, for at a glance they seem merely bumps on the huge hills.

West Kennet long barrow entrance. A huge long barrow open to the public, nr Marlborough, Wilts.

'Causewayed camps' are another work of Neolithic times. The best known is perhaps Windmill Hill near Avebury, a considerable area of chalk downland enclosed by several broken banks and ditches. They are thought to have been cattle-pounds. They are not always, though often, on hill tops. A ploughed-out example was recently discovered and excavated in a *low-lying* meadow close to the River Thames at Staines, Middlesex.

Many Neolithic sites, levelled by the work of later inhabitants, have been found as 'crop-marks' on air photographs. The silted-up ditches often afford deeper and moister root-hold, especially for corn crops, which remain dark green when a dry spell has parched and browned the rest of the field. From the air, or

a suitably high viewpoint on the ground, such prehistoric features—ditches, pits, post-holes of houses—are often to be seen under standing crops when there is no more trace left on the surface. Many are still to be discovered, never having been noticed or photographed at exactly the right moment. Among them are the 'cursuses', narrow strips of land, often several hundred yards (or even miles!) long, bounded by shallow ditches. Their use is unknown, but race-tracks or processional ways have been guessed at. There is one at Stonehenge.

A ploughed field after rain, in many of our long-farmed areas, will sometimes yield a scatter of Neolithic, or later, worked flints. Many are not easily recognizable, but neatly worked leaf-shaped arrow-heads a couple of inches long are especially typical of this period, though not easy to find unless you have luck.

EARLY BRONZE AGE
(about 1500–900 B.C.)

This period is specially marked by stone monuments, of which the

Stonehenge, most famous stone circle in the world. The large sarsens, and smaller blue stones from Wales

26

Avebury, older, nearly as well known. Part of one of the circles

best known are 'henges', ditched and banked circular enclosures, sometimes with rows or circles of standing stones. Avebury and Stonehenge, Wiltshire; Arbor Low, Derbyshire; Thornborough Rings, Yorkshire, are examples. The first two are the largest and most striking.

Stonehenge axe and dagger engraving, proving Mediterranean connections

Round barrows, varying from imposingly large mounds to slight, scarcely perceptible bumps in pasture, ploughland or heath, are Bronze Age burial monuments, generally in the first place for a single individual, though later Bronze Age people often buried the ashes of their cremated dead in and about them. They are the commonest of barrows and they often occur in striking groups, on a skyline, and many are visible from

roads crossing Salisbury Plain and the Wiltshire Downs. Represented in many counties, for instance Lancashire, Yorkshire and Derbyshire, they are really concentrated in the south and west of England. Hundreds have been excavated, and have generally yielded one or two burials, perhaps with a beaker (drinking-vessel) or other pottery, and a couple of barbed flint arrowheads—seldom anything of rarity or value. They often have later remains, sometimes in or under pottery urns, pushed into them.

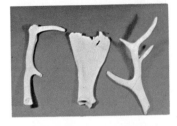

The tools used by ancient Britons:
(a) deer-horn pick and bone shovel;
(b) potsherds or shards, the commonest find; (c) axe and hammers

27

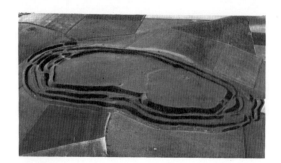

Maiden Castle, an Iron Age fort in Dorset

When you see a long or round barrow you must think of it as shining white on the dark hills: that's how it was.

In the West Country, as on Dartmoor, there are 'stone rows'—long lines of standing stones—of which the use is unknown, but which seem to mark, as do the ditches of the cursuses (which are certainly earlier), an avenue or processional way. At Grim's Pound, on Dartmoor, there is a large group of Bronze Age 'hut circles' of huge granite blocks. These are only one example of very many to be found here and there in rocky country. They are the walls of biggish round huts, probably once with a timber and thatch, or turf, roof supported on posts and rafters. Some on Dartmoor are associated with old stream-tin workings, which show as rough piles of rubble in stream valleys near by. Tin is essential for the best bronze, to make weapons and tools, though it was worked here in stream gravels up to much later times. Apart from these, we have scarcely any Bronze Age settlements or dwellings, and it is

thought that the people were herdsmen and shepherds, following their flocks and living in skin tents or wooden shelters which would leave no trace.

EARLY IRON AGE (700–45 B.C.)

Though the Roman Conquest ended the prehistoric period in most of England and Wales, 'prehistory' still continued beyond the Roman walls, in Scotland and Ireland, for several centuries. Numerous isolated settlements and farmsteads which had solidly built permanent timber buildings are known, gener-

A fallen defender. The tip of a Roman spear lies in the spine of a British fighter at Maiden Castle

Oldest White Horse is at Uffington in Berks.

ally in the first instance from crop-marks. In rocky country there are the 'castles' (dry-stone buildings), evidently designed for defence, as at Chun and Chysoyster in Cornwall and the 'brochs' of the highlands and islands of Scotland. The most striking and common evidences of the period, however, are the 'camps' and hill forts, which crown many hills all over Great Britain. They are enormous and impressive. In the south and east these are earthworks, often with several lines of defence formed by banks and ditches and enclosing several acres of land. In only a few cases do they seem to have contained buildings, other than lightly constructed huts. The period of the immediately pre-Roman Celtic peoples seem to have been a time of unrest and inter-tribal wars and forays. The 'camps' seem to have been defended strongholds to which a whole tribe would retire in time of danger with all its cattle and other livestock. Some, such as Maiden Castle near Dorchester, are known to have been defended against the Roman armies.

Hillsides all over the chalk country are covered with 'lynchets', the banks of Celtic and later culti-vations. 'Positive' lynchets are formed wherever the soil is ploughed on a steepish slope, by downwash of loosened earth to the lower boundary of the field, while a 'negative' lynchet forms by the fall-ing and washing away of soil from the upper margin. Now completely grassed or ploughed over, they nevertheless clearly mark pre-historic field systems which were tilled, probably for at least some centuries. Generally called Celtic Fields, most appear to be of the Iron Age, though cultivations may have started much earlier than this. Their squarish open shapes contrast with the narrow strips of medieval cultivation.

The Long Man of Wilmington, 230 feet high, cut into the chalk of Sussex

29

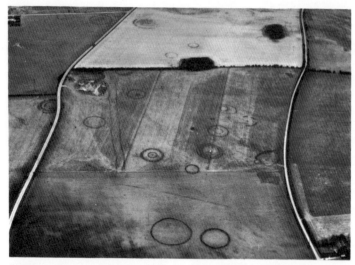

Seeing into the ground. Crop marks reveal (under special conditions) the works buried under the soil

Ancient farmers made these: (1) square Celtic fields and (2) Saxon lynchets

Prehistoric industry has been mentioned in connection with Dartmoor tin-streaming. Before the metal ages of bronze and iron there were flint-mines. Those of Neolithic age, at Grimes Graves, near Brandon in Suffolk, and at Cissbury in Sussex, are perhaps the best known. Flint was an important material for cutting-tools right up into the metal ages and beyond. The best flint was often to be found some distance below the surface. The Grimes Graves mines are funnel-shaped shafts, several yards across, from which, at a depth of about twenty feet or more from the surface, narrow mine galleries radiate, following the flint seam. Before excavation there is only a shallow, saucer-shaped depression to be seen, with a raised rim of chalk rubble and flint-working waste, but a considerable area may be pock-marked with them, and the working galleries of one shaft may meet those of the next under-ground.

West and north of a line from the Bristol Channel to the Tees there were many Neolithic stone-axe factories. The best stone for ground and polished axes was a tough crystalline rock, and this kind is only found in the Highland Zone, where it was quarried, worked and exported to the users. Famous examples of factory sites are in Cumberland, North Wales, Cornwall, and even Northern Ireland, from all of which the products have been brought from afar. The stones of the Avebury Circle are local Marlborough

Downs sarsen quartzite. The same material was transported, often in huge blocks, twenty miles south to Stonehenge. The 'Blue Stones' of the inner circle at Stonehenge came originally from Pembrokeshire—perhaps on rafts or boats by sea to Christchurch and then up the Hampshire Avon.

The end of prehistory. Hadrian's Wall, the Roman boundary, 73 miles, from Newcastle (Wallsend) to the Solway Firth, dated about the first century A.D.

In so short an essay only a very few examples can be given of what to look for as remains of prehistoric Britain, that is, pre-Roman. There are many more kinds of barrows or burial places, e.g. circular disc barrows, bowl barrows, bell barrows, of which you may read more in other books. The rule must be to be suspicious of all features—gullies, depressions, bumps on the ground—and to ask yourself if they mean something or had a purpose.

5: On Track and Road

NEXT time you see a footpath across a field have a look to see if it is straight. Probably it wanders about. The people first to walk that way avoided bumps, nettle-beds, stony ground or wet patches, and those that followed took the easy course —they followed the beaten track.

Trackways behave in the same way, and many of our early roads followed those tracks. The only difference is in the scale of the obstacles avoided. Instead of ant-hills, nettles and wet patches, the tracks avoided real hills, forest and marsh. When the nettles die and the wet patches dry up men go on following the same path because it is made. Where tracks and roads are concerned the hills remain, but the forests may be cut down and the marshes drained. Yet a keen eye will probably see where the obstacles once were, because the lines of our roads still 'avoid' them.

Man must move. The most ancient evidences of actual road making in Britain date from the end of the Stone Age and the beginning of the Bronze Age about four thousand years ago. They are in the form of brushwood and split logs laid over a marshy surface now covered by many centuries' deposits of peat. They were noticed when the peat was cut for fuel and for commercial purposes in the Somerset plains. Note the place-name MERE (or LAKE) on the Somerset-Wiltshire borders.

One of the earliest metalled road-ways was found by archaeologists a the entrance to an Iron Age fortified camp at Oldbury in Kent (metalled means 'made' with broken stone). It was only a short length at a point near the entrance, where the road would suffer most wear. Little of this road could be seen above ground, but an interesting fact emerged—the line of the metalling was in line with an existing field track which was used to mark the parish boundary when these were settled many hundreds of years ago. Thus the boundary represents the line of the long-disused prehistoric road.

Now road systems come and go; they are developed and may then fall out of use. They may fall out of use in parts only or they may be diverted, but it is usually possible to spot the original line, especially if you use a map. Often old tracks or Roman roads are so marked on maps. (See note on maps at end of book.)

Have a look at the map where the little town of Edenbridge lies on the border between Kent and

Ridgeway. Part of the Berkshire route running for many miles along the down tops

Surrey, and you will see that the main street lies on the line of a Roman road from London to the south coast called Stane Street. A little to the south of the town the modern road branches east and west, but a little track still continues the ancient line. North of the town the line of the old road is still in use as a short length of modern road near Titsey Hill and Biggin Hill. This continuing use of lengths of old road is something that can be noted almost everywhere in Britain, even in busy cities. Edgware Road and Oxford Street in London are examples, for they lie on the Roman road from Dover to the north-west, called Watling Street.

G. K. Chesterton once wrote that the 'rolling English drunkard made the rolling English road', but his history is wrong. There were very good reasons for all the twists and turns. Remember that except for a few recently built by-passes and motorways our roads came into use long before the invention of the motor-car.

If you use your eyes and just a little knowledge of history and a bit of detective work on place-names you will probably be able to see why the roads of today came to be where they are and why they often make strange and, at first sight, senseless turns. The growth and abandonment of roads and their diversions, however, have come at many different times and for different reasons.

You must imagine yourself on foot, or at best on a pony, for the wheel had hardly come into use, and you are living well before the time of the Roman Conquest. Much of the country is thickly forested, and by the streams and rivers there are many miles of swamp land. No one has begun to drain the river-meadows, and the only farming is on naturally well-drained open land. You will probably be a farmer yourself, scratching a living somewhere on the light earth which covers the chalk downs of southern England. Largely the farm will be self-supporting, but you will want to trade with your nearest neighbours and to buy with your produce such things as hard stone axes which you cannot yourself produce.

To save yourself the effort of climbing up and down hill, and to avoid pushing your way through scrub trees, when you travel you will keep to the crests of the chalk hills. Your neighbours and the men who trade in axes, hides and the honey of wild bees will be doing the same; and so will grow up the long ridgeway tracks which still run across the uplands in our own time.

One great ridgeway is called the Berkshire Ridgeway and it can be

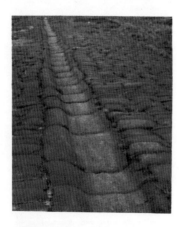

Roman braking system. A rare piece of Roman road, showing groove for pole-brake

The Roman roads, straight and true, run across country. There are about 7,000 traceable miles of them. This is the Fosse Way in Leicestershire

seen running along the ridges for mile on mile. There are branches like the one which follows the tongue of chalk which, just to the west of Stonehenge, runs between the valleys of the rivers Avon and Wylye.

From the Humber in the north to the Mendips in the south-west runs another track—the Jurassic Way—up along the Lincoln Edge, and for a large part of its length sticking to the junction of two geological formations (the Lias and the Oolite). Many such ancient routes are to be seen and traced in the form of grass-grown tracks; short stretches are still in everyday use. They were (and are) spread like a web across England, and most are marked on good maps.

Travel and transport could not remain for ever on the ridges, and ancient roadways will be seen

twisting along at the foot or on the lower slopes of lines of steep hills. An example is the Pilgrims' Way from Dover to beyond Winchester, which is far older than any religious pilgrimage. It runs at the foot of the chalk hills just above the level at which the chalk joins clay, and where there is a line of permanent springs of fresh water—the spring line.

Where the little rivers cut the chalk hills the road turns up either side of the valley. The travellers who used the road were clearly looking for easy crossings over the rivers and marshes and they crossed at *fords*. In later times there sprang up little settlements at these crossings, and on the River Darent we have names like Ot*ford*, Eyns*ford* and Dart*ford*.

The Pilgrims' Way, like other early roads of its kind, is often double; that is, there are two versions of the road, one higher up the hillside than the other. These were the Summer Ways and the Winter Ways. The modern route alternates between one and the other.

Clapper bridge, an early style, for man and beast. This is in Devonshire

You will find remains of old tracks coming cross-wise down the steep hillsides joining the ridgeways to the hill-foot roads and to stopping places. Few are in use today, but they still stand out clearly on the grassy hillsides. This is partly because, when the tracks were in use and the surface had been loosened by the feet of men and animals, the rain scoured and cut them deeply into the hillsides. In the chalk counties it is a splendid sight to see these hillsides, in the low evening sunlight, gashed by these shadow-filled ways running into the valleys.

Often in hilly country you will be able to recognize an old road just because it has been cut down in this way by storm water. Sometimes the surface of the road now lies at the bottom of a deep trench carved into the rock. A modern road of recent construction does not permit such down-cutting, for the surface is protected by a hard artificial skin. At the approaches to towns in hilly parts you can sometimes see a regular network of old tracks converging from various points of the compass. You can say, roughly, that any deep road is an old road; indeed many are called today Hollow Lanes.

Everyone knows of the roads built by the Romans. Somehow the road engineers contrived—maybe by sighting along rows of ranging poles—to construct great lengths of road in very direct lines, though they too had to consider where the road could run most easily. Often they used stretches of earlier roads, but their purpose was not to promote trade. Roman roads were principally made so that troops could be moved quickly about the country. In a motor-car today we travel very fast along extensive stretches of Roman roads still in use and we see new scenery every few minutes, but imagine how dull it must have been for a Roman soldier carrying his pack as he marched for miles on a road with hardly a turning.

The Romans were the first people in Britain to do more than just follow trackways and the first people to *construct* new roads; these roads had a camber to their surface and were composed of successive layers of stone, sand and gravel. They were also provided with drainage ditches and banks on either side. It is this care in construction as well as the convenience of the routes chosen that have led to so many Roman roads being still in use today. As you pass along a Roman road, look for the depressions in the ground on either side from which road-making material was dug.

The Romans too were the first people to attempt to make regular roads across waterlogged ground, for they built extensive causeways over low-lying ground in order that their troops should be able to reach and garrison certain of their fortified towns and strongpoints. Nothing like these causeways was built again until the Normans built causeways across the fens from Ely in the direction of Cambridge. Go to the peak of a hill on a Roman road and look behind you and in front and you will see (especially in the winter) how the road leaps on and on, straight and true.

When the legions left and the Saxons settled in the river valleys the whole way of life of our ancestors changed. Life became far more localized. People were tied to their fields and the journeys they had to make were only to neighbours, to feudal courts and to manor houses, and to the fields. Many old roads then fell out of use and became grass grown, though their courses can still be traced and they continued to be of use as boundaries and farm ways.

The majority of Cornish, Welsh and Scottish lanes belonging to this time will still be found to form a network connecting separated farms, but the people of most of England built their houses together in villages with big open fields around them. These little communities were complete in themselves with roads to the fields and to the water-mills.

The fords again (note Ox-ford) began to give way to narrow bridges, chiefly for the use of pack-horses, though a few heavy wagons began to be used. A great many of these well-built bridges, sometimes a little out of 'true' with the direction of the earlier road, were erected in the thirteenth, fourteenth and fifteenth centuries and many are still in use. But they are only wide enough for one vehicle at a time, and it is worth noting how often the parapets have little recesses to which pedestrians could retreat for safety when a wagon passed.

There was little need or inclination to repair roads from one village to another, and attempts to fill in holes with loose stones and brushwood were not very successful. When a track became muddy or

Toll house (road gate removed) erected by a Turnpike Trust to collect road-building costs

Old roads, splayed on the outskirts of town, each avoiding the mud and ruts of previous travellers

the going difficult up a hill it was advisable to pick a new way somewhat to one side, and when that became impassable (perhaps by the fall of a tree) to choose another a few paces away. In this way the roads, such as they were, became extremely wide, and often today you may find a modern road surface of normal width running between hedges which are sixty to eighty feet or more apart. On steep hillsides deeply gullied alternative routes can often be seen.

Rather similar are the tracks which were trodden by herds of sheep and cattle as they were driven to the market town. These droveways, as they are called, were wide enough to provide grazing on either side of the main pathway; they can be seen cutting across country, hedged maybe, but seldom used now except by tractors and walkers. As you pass the outskirts of a town you will sometimes see roads called Ox Drove or Sheep Drove.

Eventually the medieval road pattern itself changed. Something more than roads radiating to fields from the village, whose central street often widened out to make space for a regular market, became necessary. Throughout England early industries developed and required means of transport, e.g. to the ironworks in the Sussex Weald and to the stone quarries of Purbeck. In their turn these industries and their roads declined.

As time went on, thoughts began to be given to the advantages of abandoning the system of common open fields, where each man had his own strip or strips of land in different fields. For reasons of greed, or under pressures of money or farming fashion, enclosing large areas under one farmer became general. Finally the Enclosure Acts followed (the first local Enclosure Act being passed in the reign of Queen Anne) and new landowners put hedges round their estates.

There was no longer need for the roads by which strip-holders used to reach their holdings, and the roads, instead of going across fields, were diverted round them. So when today your road takes seemingly meaningless right-angled turns in the middle of open farming country you are probably following the boundary of part of an old field system.

From Tudor times onwards people began to move about more and the wealthy travelled hazardously and uncomfortably on rough roads in heavy coaches, but it could take eight or ten horses to get them under way on the unmade road surfaces. But how much they travelled is amazing!

The Turnpike Act was passed in 1663—Turnpike Trusts undertook to keep stretches of road in repair and occasionally to build new ones in return for payment of a toll by everyone who used them.

Toll bridges were also constructed, and even today a few toll payments still have to be made. Little round and octagonal houses by the roadside sometimes survive at the places where toll-gates stood.

Travel by horse-coach became popular, for one could then reach Brighton from London in something like five hours if horses were changed at regular intervals. These stages were usually at inns where food, drink and shelter were provided for man and beast, and the great coaching inns came into their own. Occasionally you will still see by an old bell-handle a faintly painted sign which reads 'Ring for Ostler'. It is amazing to record that coaches timed their arrival to the half-minute! That would be *their* time, since there was no Greenwich time signal until about 1840 and villagers kept their own time as best they could!

In many towns you may see old inns with a great entrance to a central courtyard with a gateway so high that the coach could drive right in under the arch. You may also find in the yard or stables pieces of old coach harness and even parts of the coaches themselves. Some of these inns have fine or curious names: the 'Who'd Have Thought it', the 'Elephant and Castle'. These were the golden days of romantic road names: the Great North Road, the Bath Road, the Dover Road—far better than our laconic A 1s and M 4s. Checking with your map as you coast smoothly along by car you will see from time to time abandoned coach roads running out of the modern roads, sometimes with old milestones.

Milestones are now fast disappearing. In the eighteenth century they were made compulsory to to prevent carriers overcharging. Some bear Roman numbers, others Arabic; nearly all well carved. Some use old town names: 'XIV miles to New Sarum', now Salisbury; some direct you sensibly to particular parts of cities: 'XIV miles to Hyde Park Corner', or 'to London Bridge' or 'to Bow Church'. Some are tall and cylindrical, some squared up, some rounded and some triangular; some are stone and

The welcome inn.
The Lion at Guildford
in Surrey, now
demolished. Note
coach entrance

some are cast iron. You can see Roman milestones in the British and other museums and one in position at Stanegate, Northumberland.

Direction and guide-posts are, like road repairs, a charge upon the County Council nowadays. They range from wooden posts, sometimes with a finger pointing, to the giant, rather frightening, metal plates on the motorways. In recent years town and village names and county border signs have been erected, sometimes extolling the ancient glories of the town's treasures.

The Royal Mail was first carried on the roads by post-boys on ponies, but in 1784 the first mail-coach began a service between London and Bristol, and within two years they were running on all the main roads out of London.

Again things changed. The coaches were able to average some ten miles an hour, but railway trains, which began their first passenger service in 1830, could manage eighteen miles an hour.

Gradually the trains took over the mails, and the last regular daily run by coach ceased in 1846. The railways also took passenger traffic from the turnpike roads, and the income for repairs was reduced; eventually the county councils took over the roads, freed them of tolls and undertook their upkeep. Sometimes you can spot a county boundary by a change in the road-making materials. Slowly the ideas of the great road engineer McAdam for giving roads a proper foundation of broken stone were adopted, and it was not until then that roads became usable at all times of the year.

Even if passable the roads were still inclined to be muddy in wet, and dusty in dry, weather. The introductions of tarred and bitumen surfaces and asphalt are comparatively new, and remembered by most people not much over fifty years old.

As for our most recently built roads, the by-passes and the motorways, they take no notice of history. Mechanical giants cut through and level whatever lies in their way, and they run through no particular centres of human settlement; rather their object is to avoid them. Small

Aqueduct. The Trent and Mersey Canal crossing the River Dove

Length and lock. The first industrial transport was by canal and by 1800 the network covered the land

towns and villages are still reached by leaving the new roads and taking to the ancient network of tracks and lanes.

So, wherever your road takes you in Britain, you are likely to be travelling in the steps of men and women who followed the same route many hundreds—even thousands—of years ago. When the road turns aside you may be avoiding only ghosts; you may be going through the motions of going round farms, fortresses, houses, forests, marshes, which have long ceased to exist in solid form.

Up to this point we have been concerned with Britain's road systems—as man began with tracks and roads he seems to want to finish with them, and our roads are crowded as never before. But railways cannot be ignored, are still important, and may yet be more important still. In 1963 railways had 17,000 miles of route track and employed a staff of nearly 450,000!

From the early years of the 1800's began the building of our railways,

until they threaded every part of our countryside, and they have left their marks upon it. Your journey will be a short one indeed if you do not pass over or under a score of railway bridges. Great engineers cut their way through the regions. They built embankments, they removed hills, they spanned valleys and built tunnels, with hardly any large-scale experience to guide them. They even 'made' towns like Bournemouth, Brighton and Torquay!

As railways have suffered from the competition of the motor-car, so canals suffered terribly from the arrival of trains. Already in difficulty in the mid 1800's, the canals fell easy prey to the railway promoters.

A hundred years earlier, in the 1700's, it was the canals which were carrying the burden of goods created by the Industrial Revolution. Where today all is silent, save the cry of water birds and the whistle of the fisherman's line, there was once bustle, and there were even 'express' passenger barges pulled by trotting horses.

To get your money invested in a canal was regarded as profitable as finding a gold-mine. But by the time the railways came it became plain that the money might just as well, in most cases, have been thrown into the waters of the canal.

But let us praise the men who built them and wonder at their achievements! To dig by shovel and fork several thousands of miles of canal (and, harder still, to keep them filled with water) was no mean achievement, and is reflected in the canal remains to be found in many parts of England to this day, not to mention the canals which still flourish.

If you look at a map you will notice that railways and canals appear as lines, crossed by roads. At the crossing point you will usually find a bridge carrying the road over the railway or canal or a cutting under the road. In flat country you may have to wait at a level crossing or you may even be held up by a swing-bridge over a canal or harbour entrance. If you want to explore a canal you will have to walk along one of those lines on the map; most towpaths are now footpaths. A close look at a good map will give you clues to places worth exploring. What happens when a canal has to cross a river or go up or down a hill? The answer may be an aqueduct, as at Avoncliff or Dundas on the Kennet and Avon; a tunnel, such as those at Sapperton, Blisworth or Harecastle; or a flight of locks like steps up the hill (or down it)—there is a flight of thirty locks at Devizes. Most of the things worth seeing on English canals are away from the roads, but are worth a short walk even along an overgrown towpath.

The most common way of discovering where a road crossed a canal is the typical 'hump-back' bridge which was built long before cars were thought of. Water always

Suspension bridge. The famous Brunel Clifton Bridge at Bristol daringly spanning the Avon Gorge and built a hundred years ago

41

has a fascination, and there are few more pleasant features of the landscape than an old canal. Most of the canals in this country were constructed at the end of the eighteenth or beginning of the nineteenth century, and their bridges, locks, wharves and cottages are among the best examples of the architecture of the period. Many have a character of their own, like the round cottages for lock-keepers and lengthsmen on the long-disused Thames and Severn Canal. Just off the main roads you will often find fascinating collections of quays, wooden cranes, wharves, docks and other canal buildings, as at Shardlow, Derbyshire. Most canals had iron mile posts and lock and bridge numbers. A mile post in a field near Saxby, Leicestershire, is all that remains of the Oakham Canal there. Other relics may be more spectacular. At Foxton, Leicestershire, you can trace the massive remains of the inclined plane up which barges were hauled in huge tanks on wheels, and of the buildings which housed the winding engines. They stand next to the 'staircase' of locks which boats use today.

Railway relics are common all over the country, and some of them need an expert eye to discover. The closing of branch lines in recent years has added many miles to the disused tracks and stations which are worth exploring, and it is surprising how quickly a railway can become overgrown and almost hidden. There is some strange attraction in a deserted station, or

a track which seems to lead from nowhere to nowhere. Railways built to serve old mines or quarries are among the most interesting. You can trace miles of them in South Wales, around the iron ore workings in Leicestershire or the small coal-mines of the Forest of Dean, for example.

Railway lines were often laid alongside waterways with the intention of saving cost and capturing the canal trade. For many miles west of Reading the Great Western Railway line to Devon and Cornwall runs alongside the Kennet and Avon Canal, which the railway company bought to prevent competition. You will find many similar examples in the Midlands, and in some cases both the railway and canal are now disused because road transport has taken over.

As railway lines close and canals are abandoned, attempts are made to preserve many of the most interesting relics. Sometimes a railway line may be kept open by enthusiastic people in order to keep old engines going or to preserve some particularly fine example of building or engineering. The 'Bluebell Line' in Sussex is a well-known example, with its beautifully maintained locomotives, and stations with their period fittings (including posters). The Tal-y-Llyn railway in Wales not only uses some of the oldest narrow-gauge engines and coaches still in existence (superbly renovated), but passes through countryside which is as spectacular as any in the British Isles. The Tal-y-Llyn railway is made even more

Railways overtake canals

interesting by its narrow-gauge railway museum at Towyn. The Ffestiniog railway, also in North Wales, was built to serve the slate quarries, and it has been revived by railway enthusiasts. A small collection of relics of the line can be seen in its station at Portmadoc.

Many museums contain collections devoted to the history of transport, and not all of them are in large towns. Crick, in Derbyshire, has a tramway museum, and at Brockham, near Dorking, Surrey, there is a narrow-gauge railway

museum. The Yieldingtree Railway Museum Trust is at Bleadon and Uphill station, near Weston-super-Mare. Perhaps the most unexpected collection of railway relics is the museum of industrial locomotives at Penrhyn Castle, which also houses a collection of a thousand dolls. There are railway museums at York and Swindon, and the finest collection of all at the Transport Museum at Clapham, London. Sometimes you will come across individual relics like the Wantage Tramway locomotive, which stands beside the platform of Wantage Road station, Berkshire, or the famous 'Locomotion 1' from the Stockton and Darlington Railway, preserved at Darlington station.

Motor-cars have already become 'museum pieces', and the magnificent Montagu collection can be seen in three parts at Brighton, Beaulieu and Measham. Bristol Museum has a collection of cars and also a very beautiful gipsy caravan. Although hardly a means of transport in the usual sense, the military tank is a development from

Snow fences are erected in hill country in winter time to prevent drifting on to the roads

The age of rail. Trains bridged rivers and channels with splendid bridges:
(*left*) Brunel's Saltash Bridge in Cornwall; (*right*) Telford's Menai Bridge to Holyhead

the motor-car and so the tank museum at Bovington Camp, Dorset, deserves mention. Another museum run by the services is the Fleet Air Arm Museum at Yeovilton, near Ilchester, Somerset. The finest collection of aircraft is that kept by the Shuttleworth Trust at Old Warden Aerodrome, near Biggleswade, Bedfordshire, where the exhibits are maintained in working order and flown regularly. The collection also includes bicycles. A Sunderland flying-boat is kept at Pembroke Dock in South Wales, where it is open to the public at specified times.

Relics of canals and waterways seldom appear in museum collections, but there is a waterways museum on the Grand Union Canal at Stoke Bruerne, Northamptonshire. An exciting example of a 'living museum' is the Stratford-on-Avon Canal, rescued from dereliction and restored by volunteers, and now owned and run by the National Trust.

The canal bridge is roadless and the pumping station is semi-retired

Motorways are now essential and here are two: the M1 at Collingtree,
Northamptonshire, and the M2 Medway Towns Road at Bottom Pond in Kent

6: Village and Cottage

COMING into a village or town by road is probably the best way to begin to discover what is to be found there, for most places grew up along the lines of communication, and for centuries rivers and 'ways' were the only way of travelling across country. Have you ever noticed how different places look when you see them from the railway? This is because the railways were not built until the nineteenth century, and by that time most places had already been in existence for a very long time. The railways were looking in from 'outside'. The Romans were the first to build *towns* in this country, and the best place to go for a Roman town is St Albans in Hertfordshire. You can still find places where people lived together before the Romans came. The cluster of stone huts on the Cornish moors at Chysoyster give a good idea of what a prehistoric village was like, and a film has been made of a reconstructed village at Woodborough, Wiltshire.

The Romans began building their towns by laying out the roads, and these were nearly always straight, crossing each other at right angles. If you find two straight main roads crossing at right angles in the middle of a town, as at Oxford, then look for other clues which will tell you whether it was first built by the Romans. If the name ends in 'caster', 'cester' or 'chester', as Cirencester or Tadcaster, then you may be sure it was Roman. Most Roman remains are buried under later building, but you can still see pieces of Roman building such as the city wall in Colchester or parts of forts on the astonishing seventy-three miles long Hadrian's Wall, and some Roman towns such as Urivonium and Verulamium (St Albans) have been partly uncovered.

Names also give a clue to the towns and villages where the Vikings, the next invaders after the Romans, settled. They came from across the North Sea and travelled up the rivers on the eastern side of the country.

Roman town plan and walls as seen from the air at Silchester, Hants

46

Richmond Castle, in Yorks., standing high and defended by the river; (*right*) Blenheim Palace at Woodstock, Oxon., one of the great houses and gardens of England

Warwick Castle; this part is called Caesar's Tower

Gardens of the big house, scattered around the home. Here are at least five gardens at Nuneham Courtenay, Oxon.

The Scandinavian word for town is 'by'; if you drive from Melton Mowbray to Leicester you will notice villages along the River Wreak — Ashfordby, Kirby, Rotherby, Brooksby, Rearsby—which prove that the Danish invaders travelled up the river and settled there. Many villages owe their origins to Saxon settlers —farmers or churchmen—although very few Saxon buildings (other than churches) survive because they were built mostly of wood. If you read an English translation of the great Saxon poem *Beowulf* you will get a vivid impression of life in Saxon times, centred round the wooden 'hall'. One of the oddities of history is the way in which the hall has shrunk from being the whole building to the awkward space between the stairs and the front door in most modern houses. Another survival from Saxon times is the roof 'finial'—the decorative tile at the top of the gable. This is the modern equivalent of the antlers with which the Saxons decorated the ends of their roofs. Towns and villages grew rapidly in the Middle Ages, and many of the names in use today come from this

A ' lost ' village discovered from the air at Lower Burstow, Bucks.

Cruck cottage (now demolished) at Sutton Bonington, Notts. Built like a tent in brick, many of these medieval cottages remain

time. Lands, including villages, often belonged to particular families and their names survive in many village names, like Stanton Harcourt, Oxfordshire. Stanton is a common name meaning 'standing stone', so that the village name means 'standing stones belonging to the Harcourt family'. If the manor belonged to the church it might be called 'Bishopstone' (Bishopstown), and the king's

property can be traced in names like Kingston, Kingsbridge, Kingswood, Kingswear and so on.

Other names indicate trades which flourished in the Middle Ages. Saffron Walden is an example, saffron being a dye which was used there. Street names can tell you ancient uses (e.g. Ferry Road, now leading to a bridge, at Rye), mark the site of things which disappeared long ago (New Canal Street, Salisbury), or indicate a trade carried on there (Knifesmith Gate, Chesterfield). The number of 'gates' shows how many towns were once walled. Totnes, Devon, is a good example of a walled town with parts of the wall and gates still to be seen, and Tenby, Pembrokeshire, is another. 'Gallowtree Gate', Leicester, is a name which tells its own story: 'Monday Market Street', 'Apple Market', 'Sheep Fair', 'Cloth Fair', 'Bull Ring', 'Quaker Lane', 'Station Road' also speak volumes.

The Romans built their roads and towns, and the 'villas' which were the centres of farm estates. Not much remains of these, but the Normans who came in the eleventh century left more massive and lasting monuments. The remains of the great Norman castles are scattered over the country from Northumberland to Cornwall. These were built as garrisons, as you can tell from the thick walls and small windows, but a more peaceful way of life was beginning to develop. The remains of a few small houses survive from this period. Some in Lincoln show that towns were beginning to be

Jettied cottage with projecting floor, elaborate and developed timber-work. This fine example is at Coggeshall, Essex, and is called ' Paycock's House '

built, and the little manor house at Boothby Pagnell is essentially a farmhouse, marking the beginnings of agricultural development.

Manor houses grew through the Middle Ages as life became more settled. Gradually the need for fortification diminished, and the battlements which had once been a necessary defence became merely a decorative feature. Walls could be thinner, and windows larger. Stokesay Castle, Shropshire, is a good example of the half-way stage. Although it still has a wall, towers and a gatehouse, these would not have been of much help in keeping out an attacking army. By the sixteenth century the country manor house had become the country mansion, large and rambling and without any of the defensive works of the earlier castles. Also, by this time, many of the 'yeoman' farmers, tradesmen and merchants had houses of their own. They were usually small, but well enough built to last to the present time.

Towards the end of the sixteenth century new ideas were reaching this country from Italy which made medieval buildings seem very old-fashioned. Gentlemen were visiting the Continent and coming back with drawings of the remains of Roman temples, or of Italian villas built in the new 'Renaissance' style. At first they tried putting bits and pieces of decoration copied from these drawings on to their houses, and very odd some of them looked. As they began to understand more about the new style they and their architects were able to design houses which were totally different from the old ones. The old houses had been a confused mixture of gables, chimneys, doors, turrets and walls, but the new ones were simpler, with decoration carefully arranged and beautifully carved. Everywhere, in the seventeenth and eighteenth centuries, landowners from the wealthiest dukes to country squires were rebuilding their houses and mansions, and redesigning their parks and gardens. Much of the country landscape as we know it is the result of this activity, and the same thing was happening in the towns.

When a town was walled the buildings would be packed tightly together to make the most use of the space. They grew upwards and outwards until they nearly met each other across the narrow streets. In villages cottages were often built end-on to the road to prevent the village from growing too far out into valuable farm land. Before the days of cars and when only the rich had carriages a small pathway was sufficient to reach most of the houses. As towns grew and trade developed the houses of the well-to-do merchants, the larger shops and such public buildings as the corn exchange (where grain was bought and sold) or market hall would occupy the street fronts and market squares, whilst many interesting buildings were tucked away behind them. You can still find many little workshops, printers, saddlers, bakers, bootmakers, clockmakers and so on, hidden in the back alleyways of country towns. Because of this it was important for tradesmen to have a sign which they could hang outside, to be seen from the road. The well-known barber's pole is an example, but some were more original, like the painted straw hat which hangs outside a butcher's in Glastonbury, Somerset. It is worth remembering that until the last century comparatively few people could read, so that the shop signs would have to be in the form of pictures or models which people could easily understand. As soon as more people were taught to read (you will find many small schools with stones showing the date when they were built), lettering on signs and notices became much more common, and many amusing examples survive. Notices on some Dorset bridges tell you that you can be sent to another country for life if you damage the structure.

Other interesting inscriptions can be seen in churchyards, where you will find mention of ancient trades and professions as well as many interesting epitaphs. Carvings on tombstones are always worth a close look, for in addition to the thousands of cherubs, urns, skulls and so on you might find tradesmen's tools, like those on a barber's memorial at Broadway, Worcestershire, or even an early railway engine, as at Bromsgrove in the same county. The earliest tombstones and monuments in churchyards are usually from the seventeenth or eighteenth century when, because transport was so difficult, they had to be made from material to be found near at hand. Some districts had good stone, but where stone was scarce other materials had to be found. In Kent and Sussex wood was used, in Leicestershire, Cornwall and elsewhere slate, and so on. As soon as a railway or canal was built other materials were brought in and used for memorials as well as for all kinds of building. In many old towns and villages the same materials were used for centuries until, quite suddenly, new ones appear. You will usually find that this happened because of some new form of transport, although there may be other reasons.

In Coalbrookdale, Shropshire, in 1709 a man named Abraham Darby discovered a cheap way of making cast iron. One of the results of this discovery was a sudden change to the use of cast iron for all kinds of things in the villages around the foundry, from bridges to tombstones. The world's first iron bridge was built in 1777 across the River Severn near the foundry.

A 'black and white' house, the last word in timber elaboration: Kenyon Peel Hall, Lancs., now demolished

Flint and brick, flint and stone or just stone: local materials were used before modern industry and transport. This is from Suffolk

By the time it became possible to carry heavy loads of iron easily across the country thousands of different things for use in streets and buildings were being made of cast iron. They are among the most beautiful things to be seen in our towns—lamp-posts, fountains, balconies, street names, even statues. In villages the ironwork for gates, railings, inn signs and similar things was most likely to be made by the village blacksmith, hammering it out in his forge.

The skill with which local materials were used for building over many centuries did more than anything else to give different parts of Britain their own particular character. They often change quite quickly as you cross a materials boundary: thatch roofs to stone roofs; tile roofs to slate roofs. In medieval times East Anglia was one of the most prosperous parts of the country, because of the flourishing wool trade. The absence of any good local store did not deter the masons of the area. They used small blocks of flint, chipped into shape for most of the walls, only using stone for corners, door posts and so on. Watch out for beautifully patterned dressed (or cut) flint in all chalk areas, often with bonds of brick or stone. In some areas the lack of stone also led to the early development of brick building and the use of wood and plaster. The Romans used brick for their buildings in Colchester, but after they left it was nearly a thousand years

Thatch on roofs was used in the corn counties. Now thatch straw has to be specially grown, since the combine-harvester leaves little stalk

A deer on the thatch as a final flourish. Often you will see peacocks and pheasants in straw

51

Brick and tile was nice enough in the brick-earth areas, where every neighbourhood had its small industry

before the first important medieval brick building appeared. This is the lovely red-brick hall at Little Wenham, Suffolk. In Essex you will find many fine brick churches.

Wood was used for building in many parts where stone was scarce and the country was forested, particularly in Kent and Sussex, East Anglia and the west Midlands. The usual method was to make a frame of timber which was filled in with plaster, brick or any other suitable material, making the familiar black and white pattern of many old cottages. Early examples had frames made like an inverted wishbone, called a 'cruck', but as the carpenters became more skilled the panels of the frame became larger and upper storeys were projected out over the street on wooden houses, one of the best examples being Paycock's House at Coggeshall, Essex. Sometimes the plaster filling was decorated with relief moulding, called 'pargeting'. In Essex too, at Greensted, you can see a 'stave church' built with walls entirely of split trunks. Sometimes you can spot a spire tiled with wood shingles. In some districts, particularly Devon, shortage of other materials led to cottages

Weatherboarded cottages are common in Kent and East Anglia. This one is at Tenterden in Kent

being built from a mixture of mud and even cow-dung, whitewashed over.

The problem of roofing was solved in many different ways. The cottages of the Yorkshire Dales have great slabs of stone for their roofs, whilst the farms and houses along the Wiltshire and Berkshire Downs still use the straw from the great cornfields in many lovely patterns, adding the flourish of a

Pargeting was a common ornament in East Anglia: a decorative plaster flourish. This example is at Lavenham, Suffolk

52

bird or even a deer on the ridges. Even flint is scarce in this district, so that much of the building was done with blocks of chalk, known as 'clunch'. The disadvantage of this material is that it washes away fairly easily, so that the roof thatch always overhangs the wall to protect it, and even walls around gardens and farmyards are thatched. In Cornwall many of the cottage roofs are tarred or cemented over as a protection against the gales off the Atlantic. Many ingenious ways of building walls and fences were devised to overcome the difficulty of finding enough material. Where stone was very common, as in Derbyshire or the Cotswolds, it could be used for walling fields, but it was far too scarce in many parts of the country. Slabs of slate were used, like rows of tombstones, in places where slate was common, such as North Wales. Villagers on the Isle of Portland used huge lumps of their famous stone for walls and gate-posts because it is the commonest material on the island, which has very few trees.

Very refined was the style of the Georgian period, the eighteenth-century age of good taste

Brick, flint and elegance at Goring, Oxon.

Village shops were romantic caves of merchandise: (1) butcher; (2) chemist

Evidence of the crafts and skills which developed in different localities over the centuries still gives character to many towns and villages. Sometimes this might be quite spectacular, like the chimneys, engine houses and spoil heaps of the disused Cornish tin-mines of villages like Botallack, or the pit workings which rise out of the trees and cottages of Charnwood Forest. More often you will discover unusual trades practised in undistinguished buildings hidden away in the back streets, often in a place occupied in this way for centuries. Brentford, Middlesex, has a vellum factory set up by the Thames in the days when Brentford was a country town. Loughborough still has a bell foundry and a rope walk where the bell ropes, with their fascinating colours, are plaited. It is surprising how many ancient crafts are still carried on in this way, but new ones can be equally interesting. Village blacksmiths still exist, but often they have become mechanics engaged in the repair of agricultural machinery, and their yards, full of

Power from water. Laxey Great Wheel in the Isle of Man is the largest water-wheel in Britain. It was built in 1854

bits and pieces of implements and ancient and modern tools, are as fascinating as any old-time forge. Note the local street-names. Look out for 'Rope Walk', 'Bell Yard'.

Village and small town shops are changing in the same way. 'Corn Chandlers' may still carry this description over their shop fronts, but their traditional stock-in-trade of sacks, trugs, baskets, seeds and dried pig's blood is expanding to include the needs of modern farming and horticulture. Old shops are rapidly disappearing behind the plastic fronts of the chain stores, but many retain something of local character and a feeling of nineteenth century wellbeing. Even the names of trades are changing. 'Haircutter' becomes 'hairdresser', 'tailor' becomes 'gentlemen's outfitter'. Old country grocers' and butchers' are delightful places, suggesting days when customers could spend time selecting their purchases, even though 'hygiene' was a word they may never have heard. Often they had—some still have—a cashier in a glass box reached by little boxes flying on wires across the shop. In the smaller villages, only about fifty years ago, many of the locals would never have been to a city. They lived in a self-supporting community, in which the essential trades were local—butcher, baker, tailor, blacksmith—carried on from half shops, half houses.

The buildings of towns are a sure sign of the times in which they were most prosperous. The huge, many-storeyed churches of East Anglia,

Windmill power. The wind was used as power for corn grinding where winds were more constant than water

Market crosses, butter crosses, poultry crosses, for the weekly buy and sell. This one is at Mount Sorrel in Leicestershire

which dwarf their villages (as at Long Melford and Thaxted) reflect the rich wool trade. Small Cotswold towns like Fairford and Northleach also grew from the wool trade of the late Middle Ages, and their churches are monuments to this prosperity, but the cloth weaving towns and villages of the Stroud valley are of a later date. Here, as in Yorkshire and Lancashire, the water of small rivers was harnessed to drive the mill wheels before the invention of the steam-engine. The Stroud valley is no longer a centre of the weaving trade, but the eighteenth-century mills, the mill-owners' and merchants' houses and the small stone-built cottages still line the steep sides of the valley and follow the canal which was built to serve the mills. Witney, across the Cotswolds, developed its blanket industry through the nineteenth century, and its cast-iron shop fronts and comfortable-looking houses are the result.

Other places grew more rapidly, almost from nothing, with the coming of some new trade or industry. Stourport grew up as the result of the building of the canal

linking the Midland cities with the Severn, and most of its earliest buildings are therefore Georgian. Similarly, but later, Derby and Swindon grew rapidly when the railways were built so that they acquired the character of the mid 1900's.

As new industries appeared and old ones changed or died out, so the pattern of town and village life and landscape changed. Even such a simple but essential commodity as water had far-reaching effects upon the landscape. Many villages grew up where they did for the simple reason that they had an ample water supply from well or spring. Sufficient water to drive a mill wheel was a necessity before the days of steam power, and many villages owe their existence to what may be now a forgotten or dried-up stream. A navigable river could bring prosperity in the days before roads or railways, and a bridge or even a ford across an important waterway almost certainly meant

Corn Exchange, where grain was bought and sold

that a town would grow there. When you travel through a town or village, ask yourself why it came to be there in the first place. The answer may appear in a road, a bridge, a pottery kiln, an ancient abbey or castle, or even an oil refinery.

The essential thing to remember about villages and towns is that they all exist because people need to live together, originally for protection but later to share in the benefits of communal life. Evidence of this is seen in many things; in the medieval castle which offered protection against marauders, just as much as in the village green which first gave the villagers common pasture land and later a cricket pitch. With the pasture went a pump, a pound—or enclosure—for stray cattle (still to be found in

ruined condition) and with the growth of law and order a village lock-up like the one at Breedon-on-the-Hill, Leicestershire. Other forms of punishment, such as stocks, remain in many places. A concern for the less fortunate members of the community is expressed in the almshouses and charity schools which were founded from the Middle Ages onwards. Ewelme, Oxfordshire, possesses a fine example of both, still in use. The benefits of living together may be seen in such details as the communal ovens in the Pembrokeshire villages of Lamphey and Carew. A whole medieval village has been preserved by the National Trust at Lacock in Wiltshire.

In the last century an increase in wealth and knowledge led to the provision of water supplies, sewerage and gas for lighting or domestic use. Even small towns like Much Wenlock, Shropshire, acquired their own gasworks. Now we are seeing electricity pylons bringing more changes, while underground run oil pipelines. The new and old together make up a landscape of incredible variety and interest, from the layout of whole towns to the smallest detail.

At the end they were laid away, not always in one piece, as this tombstone explains

SACRED

TO THE MEMORY OF THOMAS SCAIFE

late an Engineer on the Birmingham and Gloucester Railway who lost his life at Bromsgrove Station, by the Explosion of an Engine Boiler on Tuesday the 10 of November 1840.

7: Churches Pointing to the Sky

IF YOU asked where was the greatest art gallery in Britain, you would be surprised to be told—and it is true—'in the open fields and villages'. In other words, our churches and their treasures.

The great cathedrals that dominate the landscape in many parts of the country never fail to attract large numbers of visitors, but the thousands of smaller churches of the villages and towns, equally ancient, are often passed by unnoticed, although there are nine thousand ancient churches in England. They date from almost A.D. 500 to A.D. 1550, and were built during a thousand years. The early Christians had a saying, 'Beauty is not on my countenance but within me', and this can truly be said of many village churches, which may contain treasures of early craftsmanship in wood or stone, in glass or painting.

The cathedral, a symbol of the authority of the bishop, was the preserve of the dean and canons, but the village church was for the humble folk of the countryside. Through the centuries the village grew up around the church, which you will notice is often pin-pointed from a distance by a lofty tower and spire. Their church was the focal point of the villagers' lives, the centre of their social as well as their religious activities. At the font, which always stood near the main door, they were baptized; in the porch they were married, and after death they were buried in the churchyard, or if they were local gentry they were laid to rest in a tomb within the church. Villages were isolated; so much so that those who lived in them rarely went beyond the parish boundary.

Garden, church and thatch: a man-made 'treasure' at Tarrant Hinton, Dorset

River, church and castle: a perfect scene at West Tanfield, Yorks.

Church and manor at Brympton d'Evercy, Som.

Minstrels sing from a stone capital. In stone and wood (even including pew ends) the churches are rich in scenes from life

Guild carvings representing trades were frequently placed in the nave, the people's part of the church. Here is a harpist and a fiddler

In its simplest and earliest form the parish church consisted of two parts; the chancel at its east end, in which the priest performed the religious offices, with the altar its most important feature; and the nave, in which the ordinary people assembled for worship, and where they held feasts or church-ales followed by dancing and merry-making at Christmas, Easter and other festivals. On the parapet of Cirencester Church, Gloucestershire, are some thirty-eight carvings that represent revellers at a church-ale; most of them are playing musical instruments such as the tabor, the rebec and the pipe—one of the figures bears the legend 'Be merry'.

An important part was played by the various guilds that were attached to the church. They were of two kinds: the religious guilds which were founded for the mutual benefit of the brethren and for works of piety and charity, and the guilds of merchants, tradesmen and craftsmen which looked after the interests of smiths, bakers, clothiers, dyers, musicians and other workers. The guilds had their own altars in the parish church, and in the fifteenth century they were building their own chapels there, where they gathered for corporate worship;

Crosses before churches were sites for preaching. Here are Saxon crosses at Sandbach, Cheshire, perhaps 1,200 years old

Rough and solid Saxon churches survive in a few places, though most were built of wood. This is at Barton-on-Humber, Lincs.

and in the nave they held their guild feasts on certain days of the year.

Of infinite variety are the village churches up and down the land, and they vary as much in size as in design. It is a far cry (eight hundred years in fact) from the small Saxon church of Bradford-on-Avon in Wiltshire, for only a handful of worshippers, to the enormous church of Lavenham in Suffolk.

Few churches built by the Saxons (up to A.D. 1050) remain in their original form, but many village churches still show clues to their Saxon foundation. This cannot be said of our cathedrals. The Saxons were skilled in the craft of shipbuilding, and their churches were generally log huts which were later swept away. You can see a rare example of Saxon timberwork in Greensted church in Essex, where the walls consist of oaken trunks split lengthwise. The surviving examples of stone churches built by the Saxons show that their masoncraft was rude and unskilled

and lacked the great principles of construction. Often, as you can see, they imitated wooden buildings. The seventh-century church of Brixworth in Northamptonshire, an important example of Saxon work, is built largely of bricks from Roman ruins in the vicinity. In its original state it must have been one of the most splendid churches of the period, for there were aisles (long since destroyed) on each side

A stave church, a unique Saxon building, still stands at Greensted-juxta-Ongar in Essex. The nave is built of oak trunks split lengthwise

An astonishing brick church, with a thatched nave, at Burgh St Peter in Norfolk. Failing stone, local materials must be used

Elegance in stone, at Saxby, Leics.

A soaring stone tower at Bickleigh, nr Tiverton, Devon

A lantern of light in glass, flint and stone, is this late church raised by the gifts of the wool merchants of Lavenham, Suffolk

of the nave. (If you don't know the parts of a church, look at the plan on page 67.)

Earlier than these is the only British church of undoubted Roman origin whose plan is still to be seen—that at Silchester in Hampshire, the great Roman centre, now a stretch of bumpy fields surrounded by a crumbling but still weighty wall. Here and there, scattered mostly in the

'Celtic fringes' in which the Britons lived quietly during the Dark Ages when the Romans were departing, are stone crosses, sometimes mysteriously inscribed, at which missionaries and saints preached. Several of these crosses are to be seen in Cornwall, where they have survived for nearly two thousand years. In ancient churchyards you will occasionally see

Towers are not always square and each region has its local style. Here is a modified round tower from Intwood, Norfolk

Many kinds of roofs glorify our churches and this is called a wagon roof. It is at Muchelney in Somerset

Timber spires and turrets, shingle covered, are frequent in Kent and Sussex. This is at Old Romney, Kent

Stonemasons and wood-carvers made tombs of great splendour and colour. This is the famous Culpeper Monument at Goudhurst in Kent

crosses which existed long before a church was built. Two famous Saxon examples are at Bewcastle in Cumberland and Hexham in Northumberland. At Whithorn, in the south-west Scottish lowlands, is a fine collection of early crosses.

It was in Saxon days that the parish had its origin, for the thanes or landowners were the first to build churches for the people on their estates; so the manor created the parish and the lord of the manor appointed the priest to serve the church. In due course the monasteries and cathedral bodies were under the obligation of providing churches for all who dwelt on their lands. These two causes were the origins of the village church.

The enormous outburst of building activity that prevailed for half a century after the Norman Conquest left the village churches untouched, for castles, abbeys and cathedrals had a prior claim, and the Normans had grand ideas. Not until the early part of the twelfth century did the Normans embark upon the extensive building or rebuilding of parish churches, many of which were very simple in form. The massive columns and round arches in many churches throughout the land bear witness to the impress of Norman culture upon Saxon England; and there is little doubt that the masons who came across the Channel to rear the great abbey churches here were occasionally employed in the building of parish churches. You can see a unique imitation on a small scale of the Norman columns and piers in Durham Cathedral in Kirkby Lonsdale church, Westmorland; and the church of Norham-on-Tweed in Northumberland also seems to have been the work of masons from Durham.

During the succeeding centuries few Saxon or Norman churches remained unchanged. The church was alive and important to all people. As villages grew, more spacious churches were required; enlargements and alterations were carried out as need arose. A larger chancel would be built; aisles added to the nave, a tower erected for the bells, a porch to shelter the doorway, a vestry for the priest, a new roof to make the church weatherproof, and the walls opened up with larger windows. So that the village church of today is often the product of piecemeal rebuildings, its origins being submerged beneath later work. As you see churches you dig down through Britain's layers of history. The church of St Mary, Witney, in Oxfordshire, covers an area four times as large as it did in the twelfth century.

But the size of a church was no measure of the population. Its scale and magnificence depended very largely upon the gifts of the local landowners and gentry, and upon the wealth of the merchants and traders, and also upon the pride of the peasants. The richest county in England in the fifteenth century was Norfolk, its wealth being derived from the cloth industry. Many of the churches in that county and in Suffolk, such as Lavenham and Long Melford, owe their splendour to the benefactions of the wool traders. At Long Melford the names of many of the clothiers, at whose cost the church was built, about 1480, are inscribed on the battlements. Similarly the famous Cotswold churches of Northleach, Chipping Campden, Cirencester and Fairford are monuments of the wool industry of the fifteenth century, and of the piety of the wool merchants. In Northleach church, Gloucestershire, the nave of which was built at the expense of John Fortey, are several monumental brasses of the woolmen, who are depicted with their feet resting on a sheep or a woolsack.

When you look at an old church you must remember that you are probably looking at a building which has been much altered, not only by the process of growth and decay but by the reforms set in motion by Henry VIII when he broke with the Pope about four hundred years ago and plunged the Roman church into chaos. Thus the monasteries and the abbeys, of which only ruins remain today, were once proud and rich and flourishing, the monks a power in the land. Now only remain the

Gargoyles as rain-water spouts were an opportunity for the mason-carvers

Scratch or Mass dial. Before the days of clocks services were timed by these engraved dials. A projecting arm (not often surviving) cast a shadow for service time

melancholy ruins of such abbeys as Fountains and Rivaulx (in York-shire) or Glastonbury, in Somerset. The churches were stripped of their treasures, their money and (more important from your point of view) their colours. Down came the Great Rood or Cross and up went the Royal Arms as Henry asserted his independence; and the wall paint-ings were whitewashed over. Today these churches are less splendid but not less lovely in their quiet peace,

A font in each church, as the place of baptism, and often they are older than the building. Here is the Norman font at Hook Norton, Oxon.

in their sombre tones, in the beauty of light and shape and the texture of stone.

The actual fabric of the village church consisted largely of the local material that was ready to hand. The builders made no bones about re-using materials from the ruins of Roman settlements. Four columns in the nave of Ickleton church, Cambridgeshire, came from Roman remains close by; and in the walls of many of the churches in Col-chester in Essex is much Roman brickwork that was found in abundance in the locality. The finest churches are those built of stone from quarries in the vicinity. The quarries of Barnack in North-amptonshire were in use from Saxon times until the end of the fifteenth century. The churches of Boston and Spalding in Lincoln-shire are built of Barnack stone. And from the Ham quarries at the south-eastern end of the ridge came the freestone for the magnificent towers that grace the Somerset churches. The cost of transporting stone was so heavy that unless quarries were within easy reach use had to be made of materials found in the locality. In Essex and other counties destitute of stone, churches were constructed of flint, rubble, brick or timber. In Norfolk and Suffolk flint was largely used, and in no county are there so many timber towers and porches as in Essex. The towers are masterly examples of timber construction, and many porches of the Essex churches are delightful specimens of medieval woodwork.

Usually the tower of a parish church was square, but in many places in East Anglia the lack of stone that could be cut into square blocks for the quoins or corners led the builders to erect round towers, constructed of flint stones bound together with tough mortar. In Norfolk, where flint was the chief building material, there are no less than 120 round towers.

Upon the nature of the material depended its decorative treatment, for stones from various quarries differed in hardness and texture. The stone known as clunch lent itself to the carving of detail and ornament, whereas the granite which was used for the churches of Cornwall resisted sculptured enrichment. Exceptional in this respect is the granite church of Launceston, the south porch of which is lavishly carved with relief decoration.

From the twelfth century onwards masons enriched the churches they reared with chiselled ornament of various kinds, much of which still remains. Rough humour was common, shown, for instance, in the carving of gargoyles as waterspouts. The Normans exercised their skill mainly on the chancel arch and the south door. An amazing display of their craft is to be seen in the small church of Kilpeck in Herefordshire, where the south door is flanked by stone shafts carved with serpents, figures of warriors and intertwining foliage, and the jambs of the chancel arch are carved with figures of the Apostles. In many doorways of the same period the arch is filled with solid masonry, and the tympanum, as the space above the door is called, bears relief carving representing a figure of Christ. A notable example is that at Barfreston church in Kent, where the tympanum portrays Our Lord in the act of blessing.

After the Norman period sculptured ornament took the form of foliage, which in the fourteenth century was rendered with a close copying of nature.

From the earliest times every parish church housed a font, invariably of stone, and round, square or octagonal in shape; and the art of the sculptor was employed to make it an object worthy of its purpose. Many fonts are adorned with figures or sculpture in relief, the sides being faced with niches containing statues of saints, or with panels depicting baptism and other sacraments of the church. Sacrament fonts came into fashion in Norfolk and Suffolk in the fifteenth century, an exceptionally rich example being that at Walsoken church.

In many village churches are still to be seen stone tombs, on which rest recumbent effigies of knights and ladies, sculptured in alabaster, stone or, more rarely, wood. Being clad in the costume and head-dress of the period, they are invaluable treasures; knights and warriors wear the armour or mail that marked their military career. Originally all tomb effigies were painted in colour to impart a realistic effect. Less costly memorials are the brasses so often embedded in the pavements of our churches, the figures engraved thereon portraying the costumes of the Middle Ages.

Second in importance to the mason in the building and embellishment of the parish church was the woodworker, whose craft is seen at its best in roofs and rood-screens. Of the many varieties of timber roofs the most ingenious and attractive is the hammer-beam, so named from the hammer-shaped brackets that rest on the walls and carry posts that support the principal rafters. The hammer-beams were often carved with figures of angels, looking down upon the worshippers in the church. The counties of Norfolk and Suffolk are the home of the hammer-beam roof; that in Needham Market church in Suffolk is a masterpiece of framed construction. The churches of Devon, Somerset and Cornwall are often roofed with wagon (like wagon roofs) ceilings of

'Graffiti' or scratchings, other than masons' marks, are often found in old churches. Here is one from Ashwell, Herts., showing the spire of old St Paul's destroyed in the Fire of London

timber, divided up into numerous square panels resplendent in colour and gilding.

Rood-screens, which were more often constructed of wood than of stone, were erected to shut off the chancel from the nave of a church, and were so called from the figure of Christ crucified suspended above the screen. The wainscoted base was divided into panels, in each of which was usually painted a figure of a saint or apostle. The south-western counties are particularly rich in rood-screens; in Devonshire there are 150 or more, many of surpassing beauty. That in Hartland church is the largest in the county and exhibits the consummate skill of the fifteenth-century woodcarver. Rood-screens were originally gilded and painted in gorgeous colours. Adjacent to the rood-screens in the churches in Devon and Somerset are often to be seen timber pulpits, the design of which is related to the rood-screens. Many of them are richly carved, the sides being adorned with niches containing figures of saints. One of the most magnificent of this kind is that in Trull church, Somerset.

Before the Reformation our churches were storehouses of painted glass. As windows became more expansive the glass painter was ever ready to fill the panels with translucent pictures illustrating the Gospel story, or portraying the saints and martyrs of the Church. Unrivalled in its wealth of ancient glass is the church of Fairford in Gloucestershire, where no less than twenty-seven windows are filled with glass of the fifteenth century, depicting the life of Our Lord, together with many apostles and evangelists.

Another means of visual teaching was the mural painting. On the plastered wall surfaces of the nave incidents in the life of Our Lord and of the Virgin Mary were painted in tempera. The most common subject, however, was the Doom, a representation of the Resurrection and the Last Judgment. This generally appeared on the wall above the chancel arch. One of the largest Doom paintings now remaining is that in St Thomas's church, Salisbury. On the wall of the nave opposite the church door was often a painting of St Christopher, patron saint of travellers. Some idea of the colour treatment of an interior is to be gained at Copford church, Essex, the chancel walls of which are covered with paintings of Our Lord and the Apostles.

Village churches in all parts of the country provide the students of heraldry with happy hunting grounds. On woodwork and masonry, on tombs and brasses, coats-of-arms and heraldic devices were a means of identifying local families who had the interests of the church and parish at heart.

The great cathedrals can hardly be included in churches of the countryside, for even in the Middle Ages they stood in populous centres or cities, and were often quite unknown to village folk up and down the country. Today even the least observant of car travellers cannot but be impressed by the cathedral of Lincoln, which on its high hill dominates the country for miles around, or by the mighty pile of Durham Cathedral seated on the steep cliff above the winding Wear. From afar the Angel steeple of Canterbury Cathedral, the lofty spire of Salisbury and the central tower of York, each beckons the wayfarer to an ancient city over which the bishop of the diocese ruled in ecclesiastical state.

MASS DIALS, CONSECRATION CROSSES, MASONS' MARKS, ETC.

Carved in the stonework of many churches will be found curious markings of various kinds. On the external wall of a chancel may often be seen a mass dial, which on a sunny morn showed the hour at which the priest was to celebrate mass in the church. More frequent are consecration crosses, that mark the place where holy water was sprinkled when the building was consecrated. There is a complete series of twelve such crosses on the walls inside Crosthwaite church, Cumberland, and several are still to be seen in Edington church, Wiltshire.

Occasionally *graffiti*, or incised designs, were made in the stonework by the masons who built the church. In Leighton Buzzard church, Bedfordshire, a number of designs for traceried windows are cut in the masonry, and in Ashwell church, Hertfordshire, are many inscriptions and a remarkable drawing of Old St Paul's cathedral.

CHURCH TOWERS (LOUVRED WINDOWS; BEACONS)

On the borders of Wales and Scotland, districts that were liable to attacks by bands of marauders, the church tower served as a defensive feature. But primarily the tower was built to hold the bells that summoned the faithful to worship. The windows of the belfry stage were louvred, to permit the sound to travel afar and to keep the weather out.

The church tower often served the purpose of guiding travellers by land and sea. The lantern level of the famous Boston stump in Lincolnshire was lighted at night as a beacon to guide mariners entering the River Witham, and at Blakeney in Norfolk a separate tower was specially built to carry a beacon. In the tower of All Saints Pavement church, York, a lighted lamp was hung as a beacon for benighted wayfarers on their road to the city.

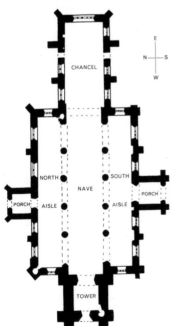

Church plan showing the principal parts

8: In Hedge, Wood and Field

ON ANY country walk, summer or winter, the most conspicuous natural objects are the trees and the birds. In summer too come the wild flowers and butterflies. You have to look harder to see even the signs left by most of our mammals, or four-footed wild beasts, but these and many other interesting creatures are there to be detected by the sharp eye.

As you spin along the motorway it is easy to think of the country as much the same everywhere. It seems to be all trees and hedgerows, and fields of grass or corn or bare earth, in an unending patchwork quilt. There are many other kinds of country besides farmland, but roads and railways do not go across them so much. There is moorland, for instance, in the North Country, woods and heaths in the south, and all round our coasts there are cliffs and sand-dunes and salt-marshes. All have different kinds of animals and plants from farmland. Even in farmland much depends on what kind of soil lies underneath.

Geographers divide Britain into Highland and Lowland zones, and the boundary between them does not just run between the north and the south, but slants in a north-easterly direction from near Exeter, on the coast of Devon, to near Scarborough on the coast of Yorkshire. North and west of this line lie the older rocks, some of them hundreds of millions of years old. These make mainly acid soils, and support miles of moorland, covered with heather and bracken and coarse moor grasses. South and east the rocks are younger, and many of them, such as the oolites of the Cotswolds and the chalk of the South Downs and Salisbury Plain, contain a great deal of lime, so that the vegetation is quite different.

The commonest tree over Britain as a whole is the oak. You may find this surprising, as it is scarce in some districts. When the Romans came they found most of Britain, especially on the heavy clay soils of the Midlands and the south, covered with oakwood. When you climb out of the clay vales on to the breezy limestone uplands, whether it is on the Cotswolds or the Clevelands or the 'White Peak' of Derbyshire, you find the oak is largely replaced by the ash as a wayside tree. The stately elms of the Midland hedgerows, frequent also in the Thames valley and East Anglia, may not be native trees; they are believed to have been introduced by some of our Celtic ancestors for the value of their branches as fodder for their cows. Our native elm is the wych-elm, which does not have the skirted

Spring scene at Stratford on Avon, showing horse-chestnut; birch in foreground

Beech in spring, looking up the smooth, greyskin bole

Giant oak in Spring. The Knightwood Oak in the New Forest, Hants

Lombardy poplar in summer breezes

Elm putting out yellow-green leaves in spring

effect of the common elm, and is commoner in the north, though by no means scarce in the south. In the valleys Lombardy poplars from the plains of Italy point like lances to the sky.

If the ash is the tree of the lime-stone hills, the mountain ash or rowan, with similar leaves but quite different orange-coloured berries, is the tree of the acid moorlands and heaths. Here also the silver birch with its attractive white bark is much commoner than on the chalk. Rowan has, however, a lime-loving relative, the whitebeam, with the same bright orange berries, but quite different leaves, whose silvery undersides glint whenever the wind is blowing. Along the riversides stands another tree with silvery leaves, the white willow, often with its branches cut back or pollarded. It is a variety of the white willow that produces the wood for cricket bats. Commoner still are pollard crack willows, named from the ease with which their twigs snap.

Hazel with catkins, and gorse in February

In spring many trees and shrubs adorn the countryside with their flowers or catkins, starting with the lemon-yellow hazel catkins as early as January. In March come the golden-yellow catkins of the sallow,

close relative of the willows, often known as 'palm' because it was formerly used to decorate churches on Palm Sunday. Sometimes it is called 'pussy willow'. Then in April, following the white sprays of blackthorn, the wild cherries spring into bloom, 'along the woodland ride, wearing white for Eastertide' as Housman put it in *A Shropshire Lad*. Wild cherry blossom is a special feature of the Chiltern beechwoods, looking most beautiful just at the time when the young green leaves of the beeches are also bursting forth. The beech is another of the special trees of chalk country, though it will also grow on sand, as it does at the famous Buckinghamshire beauty spot of Burnham Beeches. The crown of the brilliant tree and shrub blossom comes from the waves of white hawthorn (or may blossom) and horse-chestnut, saturating the air with scent, and on the crab apples in May and dog (or wild) rose, in June.

The chalk downs have their special shrubs, commoner on the slopes of the downs than anywhere else: the wayfaring-tree, with flat heads of white flowers and red berries that finally turn black in autumn; its close relative the wild guelder, with fine flat heads of purer white flowers and berries that stay a brilliant sealing-wax red; dogwood, with smaller heads of white flowers, berries of black and beautiful dull red autumn leaves that finally fall to reveal the red stems by which you can tell the dogwood all winter through. Privet too has white flowers and black berries, and on its half-evergreen leaves feed the handsome large pink-striped green caterpillars of the privet hawk-moth, which are so hard to see.

Some of our trees and shrubs are fully evergreen, and these add enormously to the pleasant contrasts of the winter landscape. A few native pinewoods survive, in such nooks of the Scottish Highlands as the Black Wood of Rannoch in Perthshire and Rothiemurchus Forest on the slopes of the Cairngorms, but Scots pine is widely planted over the rest of Britain, and grows freely on many southern heaths, such as those and occasionally even make small woods, as at Kingley Vale on the South Downs, but juniper, which is much more often a shrub than a tree, is equally at home scattered on the chalk of the southern downs and in the Highland pinewoods.

Over most of the country the two commonest evergreens are those Christmas favourites, the holly and the ivy. In the spring it is worth examining a holly tree, which flowers in late April and May, to see if it has male flowers (with *stamens* and *anthers*) or female ones (with *styles* and *stigmas*), for of course only the female flowers will produce berries for Christmas

Willows in variety in watery places

around Frensham Ponds in Surrey. Pines belong to the group of plants called conifers, because they carry their seeds in cones instead of in nuts or in berries, and while many kinds of conifer are planted, spruces, firs and larches, only two kinds are native, both of them evergreen, the yew and the juniper. Yews grow especially on limy soils, decorations. Holly is like several other plants in having separate male and female flowers, instead of flowers which are both male and female, which is more usual. Hazel is another shrub with this arrangement, but it carries the separate male and female flowers on the same plant, instead of on different ones. The familiar catkins are the

71

Oxford ragwort, the yellow high-summer flower, found in fields all over the Midlands and south

Cuckoo pint, or lords and ladies, with greenish lily-like flower, lies low on banks and will not survive picking

Teazle in winter, once commonly used for napping cloth, with the ever-present ivy

male flowers; the tiny red female ones that produce the nuts appear a little later on.

If hazel is our earliest flowering plant, ivy, our only evergreen climber, is the latest, not actually flowering until September or even October. Only in winter, when it

Ragged robin in the spring hedgerows

provides most of the green in the trees and hedgerows, does one realize how abundant is ivy in the countryside. Our other climbers, which are deciduous, dying back in winter, include traveller's joy, a species of wild clematis found in chalk and limestone districts, which is also known as old man's beard because of its grey feathery fruits; and the two bryonies, which are quite unrelated but both red-berried and poisonous, the white bryony with ivy-shaped leaves being our only native representative of the cucumber and melon family, and the black bryony with leaves like an ace of spades, our sole example of the great tropical yam family.

A poisonous plant that scrambles rather than climbs is bittersweet or woody nightshade, whose purple and yellow potato-like flowers (potatoes belong to the nightshade family) give rise to poisonous egg-shaped berries which turn from green to yellow and finally red. It must not be confused with the still more poisonous deadly nightshade or belladonna, a tall stout plant

Rosebay willowherb glows at every field-hedge and wood-clearing in July

with dull purple bell-shaped flowers and black berries the size of a small cherry. A third poisonous species is the black-berried black nightshade, with white flowers like bittersweet. It is a frequent garden weed. The attractive woodland plant and sometimes garden weed, enchanter's nightshade, is not especially poisonous (it is always inadvisable to sample any strange plant) and quite unrelated.

Among quite a number of other wild plants known to be poisonous to man or animals are the evil-looking henbane, with clammy leaves and livid yellow bell-shaped flowers; the flashy and sinister thorn-apple, with its white trumpet flowers and fruits like small horse-chestnuts; several deadly relatives of cow parsley: hemlock, the one that did for Socrates; cowbane, the one that does for unwary cows; and various water dropworts. Even the

Bee orchid lives astonishingly up to its name

handsome and common buttercups are poisonous to cattle, and so is the ragwort, food plant of the brilliant red and black cinnabar moth, whose black and yellow striped caterpillars often eat a whole plant to death.

Buttercups and yellow ragwort are among the plants that provide mass colour effects in the countryside. These floral displays start in the early spring with the white wood anemones and yellow daffodils and primroses in the still leafless woodlands, where they are later followed by the tides of bluebell. In the meadows the first mass colours come from the dandelion—how we should admire it if it were a rarity!—followed by buttercups, soon to be overtaken by the red flowerheads of sorrel. On the hedge banks late April and early May see the first of a succession of white umbellifers—plants of the carrot family with their flowers arranged in spoked umbrella-like heads—the common cow parsley, followed in late May by rough chervil and in July by hedge parsley. In woodland clearings two tall pinkish-purple flowers often make a brave show, the foxglove and the rosebay willowherb, called fireweed from its tendency to grow in woods after a fire. In damp meadows and banks June and July bring the pungent white spikes of meadow-sweet. If spring starts with yellow and white and summer continues with pinkish-purple, August brings the full purples of heather on the moors and sea-lavender on the coastal salt-marshes.

People travel hundreds of miles to see the wild flowers of the Alps, many of them little realizing that sights just as fine are to be seen at home, especially on our chalk downs and the mountain meadows of the Scottish Highlands. Too much of our downland has been ploughed up in recent years, but if you know of an unploughed stretch, perhaps on National Trust land, you will find there a superb display of wild flowers, beginning in spring with the hairy violets in late March and the cowslips in April. Later in the year such gorgeous and attractive plants as the purple clustered bell-flower and autumn gentian, the blue scabious and many kinds of orchid appear. On the mountains mid June to late July is the best time, and there is no better place to go than Ben Lawers in Perthshire, which now belongs to the National Trust for Scotland.

Orchids always attract people, partly because they are so beautiful in themselves, but partly because of their somewhat romantic associations, giving their names the overtones of tropical forests. The first and one of the commonest of our native wild orchids is the early purple, Shakespeare's 'long purples', which is widespread in woods and meadows in April and May. From then until the autumn, when the twisted white spikes of autumn lady's tresses wind up the season, a constant succession of orchids comes into bloom. Among the more striking and attractive are the pyramidal

A stoat will often streak across the road in front of you

and fragrant orchids, specialists of chalk grassland, and the white helleborine, common in the beech-woods of the southern chalk, where it is accompanied by the strange looking brown birds-nest orchid, which has no green colouring

Blue tit, coal tit, nuthatch will twist and turn in gardens

74

matter, and is what botanists call a saprophyte, feeding on decaying vegetable matter. It must not be confused with a quite distinct plant that flowers a little later, in July, the yellow birds-nest. The lady orchid is one of those curious plants which have a very restricted distribution, but is quite common where it does grow—in this case in woods in Kent, especially East Kent.

Another rare plant which is common enough where it is found is the Cornish heath, which takes the place of ordinary heather on the heathlands of the Lizard Peninsula in south Cornwall. It flowers in August, but is found scarcely anywhere else in the British Isles. Some other rarities are more local than this, but occur in quantity in widely scattered localities, as, for instance, the snakeshead or fritillary, of a few meadows in southern England, notably Magdalen Meadow at Oxford, where it is safely protected; the superb purple pasque flower of a few spots on the downs, mainly on the east side of England; and the glorious sky-blue spring gentian, which grows only in Upper Teesdale, on the borders of Durham and Yorkshire, and in that remarkable district of western Ireland, the Burren, where so many other rare and beautiful wild flowers grow. One very famous rarity is the wild peony of Steepholm, an island in the Bristol Channel; this alas is not native, but the relic of some monkish garden.

Though the flowering plants are so conspicuous, by far the greater number of our plants are flowerless. These are called *cryptogams*, including ferns, horsetails, liverworts, mosses, lichens, seaweeds and other algae, and fungi. Of these the most easily seen are the ferns, horsetails and some of the fungi—others are minute and microscopic. While many ferns have the same general pattern of the familiar male fern and bracken, with finely divided leaves or fronds, there is one that is common, at least on the west side of

Hares, with their kangaroo-like legs and loping run

75

Goldfinch will often jog along
the hedgerows in company
with you

Britain, and that has an
individual leaf. It is the
hartstongue, which fes-
toons so many Devon and
Cornish lanes. The horsetails have
whorls of thread-like 'leaves' up
their erect stems, and are actually
small survivors of a group of plants
that was much greater, in both size
and numbers, millions of years ago
when the coal measures were being
laid down. These 'living fossils'
are not to be confused with the
aquatic flowering plant known as
marestail.

Let us turn now to the animal
kingdom. Few mammals are likely
to be seen in an ordinary country
walk except rabbits, now increasing
again after the myxomatosis epi-
demic of 1953–6, hares and grey

squirrels, which were introduced
from America about seventy years
ago. In Scotland or East Anglia,
however, the native red squirrel is
still the commoner species. One
other animal shows its signs, but
is rarely seen above ground—the
mole, whose molehills are a
frequent sight in old meadows.
Another, alas, more often seen as a
corpse of the highway, is the hedge-
hog; he moves too slowly to avoid
fast motor traffic. Quick to scuttle
out of the car's way you will sometimes see the flash of a weasel or a
stoat. Deer are now common in
woodlands all over England and
Scotland, but compara-
tively rarely seen. There
are two native species, the
red and roe deer, and
three introduced species,

Lapwing, or plover, with
smart head tuft, will feed in
fields or drift across the sky
in flocks

Kestrel, above high ground, will hover while viewing for prey

the fallow, Japanese sika and muntjac or barking deer from China, which have escaped from deer parks in various places and spread themselves around. On Exmoor, the Martindale Fells of the Lake District and in the Scottish Highlands you may well come across wild red deer, but only after a good walk. It is, of course, easy enough to see what they look like at close quarters by a visit to Richmond Park, where both red and fallow deer are kept.

Our few amphibians, frogs, toads and newts, and the reptiles, snakes and lizards, are not very conspicuous objects in the countryside; an occasional adder basking in the sunshine, a lizard darting away from a sunny bank, a pond full of frogs' eggs or tadpoles, are likely to be their main contribution to the sights of an ordinary country walk. Our only poisonous snake is the adder, with its strongly marked zigzag pattern; both the grass-snake and the slow-worm are harmless. Your motto should be not to kill these beautiful creatures.

Birds are by far the most conspicuous members of the animal kingdom in the countryside,

whether as great flocks of rooks or starlings winging their way to roost, jays rasping, gulls screaming at their breeding colonies, wild geese honking overhead on migration or the quieter voices of ordinary bird song. And here too, as with the trees and wild flowers, the kinds of bird you can expect to see will depend very much on the habitat or type of country you are in. In farmland, for instance, one of the most conspicuous birds is the skylark, conspicuous not by sight but by sound, for all day from late January

Kingfisher, a beauty, will mostly be seen as a blue flash along streams

77

Pheasant, a foreigner but pertly at home, with the marauding rook

Jay, a glorious sight but a loud squawker, with the dapper great tit

78

Green woodpecker, red-headed, will cling to trees, tap, tap, and cry 'Yaffle', which it is sometimes called

to June, and again for a few weeks in the autumn, it will be pouring out its song while suspended high in the air. More conspicuous still are the rooks, jackdaws, woodpigeons, magpies and other birds that feed in the fields, and the kestrel that hovers overhead while he searches the fields below for his mouse victims. Brown partridges rise noisily from the corn stubble.

Most farmland is bordered by hedges, and the typical birds of hedgerows on a summer's day are bullfinches, chaffinches, yellowhammers and whitethroats. These are the birds of the wood edge, or, in the case of the chaffinch, of the woodland itself, for it is the woodland birds that have spread out to colonize such new habitats as hedgerows and gardens. Robin, hedge-sparrow, blue tit, wren, blackbird and song-thrush are all primarily birds of woodland. They have only within the past thousand years or less become garden birds, for only within the past few hundred years have there been any gardens for them to colonize. Other typical woodland birds are the woodpeckers, of which the two commonest are the green woodpecker or yaffle

and the great spotted or pied woodpecker. Both became rather scarce after the terrible winter of 1962–3, but are slowly recovering their numbers. The green woodpecker is one of our handsomest birds, with its yellowish-green plumage and red topknot. Pheasants in their vivid un-English colours will stray from woodland into field or road, and rise fussily. Get up early or go out late, to hear the woodland nightingales, often in broad daylight.

Up on the moors the bird life changes again, though the skylark survives from the farmland association. Where there is heather, and north of Cannock in Staffordshire, the red grouse is king of the moors, and recent research shows that it is almost wholly dependent on the heather shoots for its food supply. The red grouse stays on the moors all the year round, but in spring and summer it is joined by countless thousands of a much smaller bird, the meadow pipit, confusingly known by the older writers as the titlark—it is neither a tit nor a lark! It forms the main prey of one of our most attractive small birds of prey, the merlin, whose male is little larger than a blackbird.

Chaffinch. This is the gay cock bird; the hen is dun and demurer

Kestrels are commoner than merlins in most hill country, but our third moorland falcon, the peregrine, is now, alas, on the downgrade, as a result of eating prey contaminated with various kinds of toxic chemical used as farm pesticides. Soon, many bird-lovers fear, the peregrine crags of the northern and western hills will be left to the raven, that other large cliff-nester. Where the hills are wooded, especially in the West Country, buzzards, which once were scarce, have in the past forty years become quite common again. In parts of Devon it is no surprise to see half a dozen buzzards soaring overhead, making their lovely ringing mew-call.

Yellow wagtail (and grey wagtail) will trot, with tails twitching, near water

Raven, peregrine, buzzard, all three are cliff-nesters and as much at home on the cliffs of the sea coast as on inland crags. But by the sea they have many companions, most of them sea birds proper, who rarely or never venture inland, one of them being the red-billed chough, now virtually extinct in Cornwall but not uncommon in parts of western Wales, the Isle of Man and Ireland. The commonest of all the cliff-nesting sea birds is the herring gull, and the next commonest the fast-spreading fulmar, which looks

Yellowhammer, a blaze of gold, perches along the hedges

like a gull but is actually a petrel. Fulmars now nest even on the low cliffs of northern Norfolk, close to Sheringham and Cromer, yet a hundred years ago they were unknown away from that remotest of western Scottish Isles, St Kilda, and did not even reach isolated Foula, in the Shetlands, until 1878.

When people talk of nesting sea birds, however, they usually mean the auks, razorbill, guillemot and puffin, the cormorant and the kittiwake, that buoyant and attractive little gull. Colonies with two or more of these species are widespread round our coasts, but most frequent in the north and west. Among the most famous colonies are those on the Farne Islands off the coast of Northumberland, Berry Head near Torquay in south Devon, the Bass Rock in the Firth of Forth and Ailsa Craig in the Firth of Clyde. The last two also have gannetries, as the breeding colonies of our largest sea bird, the gannet, are called. Cormorants and shags are two more kinds of sea bird that often nest in these large mixed colonies.

Along the lower coasts, flanked by salt-marshes instead of cliffs, a quite different set of birds occurs, mainly the waders, such as curlew, redshank, dunlin and ringed plover, which are true waders, and other long-legged birds that wade, such as the heron, which comes down to the shore to feed in winter or from heronries that are not too far inland. Several more of our freshwater birds also come down to the coast in winter to feed, among them the kingfisher and the coot, while many ducks, like mallard and widgeon, are also just as much at home on salt water as on fresh. To the dedicated bird-watcher a visit to one of the east coast estuaries in the winter months, cold though it may be when the north-east wind is blowing, is a most rewarding experience. On some estuaries he will hope to find wild geese, especially the small black brents, grebes, divers and such sea-going ducks as merganser and goldeneye,

while a bag of eight or ten different species of wader, including knot, grey plover and bar-tailed godwit, would be regarded as comparatively moderate. Those who cannot reach the coast find their recreation in visiting one of the large inland reservoirs, such as Staines in Middlesex (where there is a public causeway) or the Eye Brook on the borders of Leicestershire and Rutland, where innumerable ducks and other waterfowl congregate each winter. On a really good reservoir a winter bird-watcher would hope for at least six kinds of duck, probably mallard, teal, shoveller, widgeon, pochard and tufted duck, perhaps a heron or two, with every chance of adding goldeneye, great crested grebe, goosander and perhaps pintail or smew before the day was done. Swans are everywhere increasing in numbers. A must for the bird-watcher is Peter Scott's Slimbridge (Gloucestershire) reserve, containing the world's largest collection of water-fowl.

Inevitably most of our time has been spent on the larger animals, the vertebrates, but on any walk through the country the observant can espy plenty of invertebrates, the animals without backbones. The butterflies are the most handsome and conspicuous, with such gaudy creatures as red admiral, peacock, small tortoiseshell and brimstone, and at times day-flying moths, such as a silver Y, cinnabar, and humming-bird hawk can also be seen. There are plenty of beetles too, even if few of them obtrude themselves as much as the bumbling cockchafer and may-bug, or the giant stag-beetle on a summer's evening. Bumblebees, honeybees, daddy-long-legs, hover-flies, dragon-flies, all fly or dart about on a summer day. Grasshoppers make their voices heard, and slugs and snails, or at least their handiwork, are often all too obvious. The birds are also on the look-out all the time for invertebrate food. How quick they are on the mark you can easily tell by digging up a few worms or grubs, leaving them out in the open, and retiring to watch what happens. It will not be long before an inquisitive robin or black-bird discovers an easy meal.

All this immensely complicated web of life lives in the countryside, and we tend to assume that it always has done so and always will do so. But this is far from being the case. A good many animals, birds and plants have already become extinct in Britain, and not only ones like the bear and wolf which might be harmful to human interests. Such harmless creatures as the black tern, the ruff and the beaver have ceased to breed with us. Many others have greatly decreased and almost become extinct, as the Dart-ford warbler, the wryneck and the Kentish plover, not to mention the military, monkey and other rare orchids. Manifold dangers creating disturbance, lack of balance in food supplies and shelter, threaten the wild life of the countryside, and these seem to be increasing from year to year. Felling of woodlands and hedges, draining of marshes, ploughing of downland, wide-spread and often ill-informed use of highly poisonous pesticides, ir-responsible shooting, pollution of the rivers and the atmosphere—one could go on almost indefinitely listing the harmful things we do to our countryside. Some of them, of course, have to be done, to secure a prosperous agriculture, but much nevertheless could be avoided.

It is therefore up to everyone who enjoys the countryside and its wild life to do all he can to help to preserve and conserve what remains, by obeying the rules, and by joining with others who are already helping. The rules are really quite simple. Do not deliberately kill or harm any animal or plant, unless this is really necessary because it is seriously harming human interests, or is part of a necessary agricultural operation. One cannot, for instance, stop a farmer mowing a field for hay because there are some attractive flowers growing there, nor say that a gardener must not put down slug bait if the slugs are eating his lettuces. But one can ask that in spraying against pests all possible steps are taken to ensure that no other animals are harmed, and that people do not wantonly shoot at birds, even those that do not happen to be protected.

9: Around the Farm

As YOU travel through the country-side you will be seeing Britain's greatest industry: farming. We can see our breakfasts, dinners and teas in the making. We all eat bread; here we see it growing. We drink milk; here we see the cows which manufacture it. We enjoy our meat; here we see it on the hoof.

The commonest breed of cow in the meadows of England is the Friesian, a big, deep-bodied matron with black and white patches distributed over her hide like a map. Most of the importations from Holland, the home of the Friesians, have occurred since the beginning of this century. Dairy Shorthorns, the breed which the Friesians have superseded but which were the basis of dairy farming for very many years, can be red or white or any mixture of the two colours, one of the favourite being roan, which is a kind of smeared blending of the two. The reason why farmers have preferred Friesians to Dairy Short-horns is that, by and large, Friesians give more milk.

For meat, other types of cattle are kept, an easy one to identify being the Hereford. Pure Herefords are red cattle with white faces. Black cattle and roan cattle with white faces have a Hereford for one parent, usually the father, for the white face is a characteristic which the Hereford stamps on *all* his progeny.

Look closer and you will see that Herefords have another unvarying characteristic, namely, a white stripe along the spine and down the tail. This is known to cattle-breeders as 'finching'. Two other very ancient English breeds from the same region, the West Mid-lands, also have it. These are the Longhorns and the Old Gloucester-shires. The Longhorns were once the dominant cattle of the Mid-lands but, because they took so long to mature into eatable beef, they have now become rare. Even rarer are the Old Gloucestershires, a breed which specialized in pro-ducing milk for the farmhouse Double Gloucester cheese. They are chocolate-brown, almost black, again with the white 'finching'. To see Old Gloucestershire cattle stampeding away through a bracken-clad park, as once I did, is to realize that the finching is an inheritance from wild ancestors, for it acts as a warning flash of white, like the scut of a rabbit.

In Norfolk and some other counties are the remnants of another ancient breed, the British White. They have black muzzles, black tips to their ears and tails, black eyelashes and sometimes a peppering of black dots on their

Original bull. The auroch, which became extinct in the seventeenth century, and has now been re-created by back-breeding

white hides. No doubt they are the descendants of white cattle known to have lived in pre-Roman Britain.

Other descendants of those ancient British cattle are the Chillingham herd of white cattle, which still wander wild in a large park in Northumberland. The difference between them and the domesticated British Whites is that the Chillingham cattle have horns while the British Whites do not.

During the past fifteen years or so cattle-breeders have come to accept the idea that cattle are better without horns, which can do a lot of damage to other cattle in yards and

Friesian cow—marked black and white like a map of the world—is now the most popular for milk

buildings. Some cattle are de-horned as small calves, and others have their horns sawn off under anaesthetics. The modern idea, however (and almost every breed has a scheme in operation), is to breed a polled type, which never grows any horns.

Black cattle as well as white were natives of Britain back in pre-historic times, and you can still see their descendants in the west and north. Wales has a breed called the Welsh Black; Ireland has a rather similar though smaller black breed, the Kerry; while Scotland has two black beef breeds,

Dairy shorthorn cow. Once everywhere but now less seen. This is a champion at Carlisle Show.

both without horns. One is the small, stocky, smooth-coated Aberdeen-Angus, which wins prizes at all the fatstock shows, and the other the heavier, shaggy-coated Galloway. The romantic wide-horned, long-coated Highland cattle are still frequent in the Scottish glens.

The Channel Islands of Jersey and Guernsey each has its own breed, both common in England as well, especially in the south. They give extra rich, creamy milk. You

Hereford bull, another champion, at the Shropshire Show. Note white mask

will see no cattle other than Jerseys in Jersey, or other than Guernseys in Guernsey. Jerseys are the more delicate grey-brown black in colour. The Guernsey is larger, solider, golden yellow and white. The breeds are kept strictly pure, and no animal which leaves the islands is ever allowed to come back.

A recent much-talked-of introduction to Britain has been the French Charollais. The only purebred Charollais in the country are a handful of bulls brought over in 1961 and now standing at artificial insemination centres, but many thousands of cows of different breeds have borne their calves. The idea is that Charollais sires will produce beef calves from dairy cows, there being a surplus of dairy calves! Crossbred Charollais calves are handsome little creatures, ranging in colour from pale lemon to a soft mushroom tint, often marked with white.

Now let's look at sheep. Although you may not notice a lot of them, there are millions in Britain. There are over forty different breeds, and the number increases.

Probably the most ancient of all is the little Soay sheep, which still ranges wild on the island of Soay, in the St Kilda group off western Scotland. A brownish sheep with little wool and a small carcass, it seems identical with prehistoric types whose remains have been found in Wiltshire and elsewhere. A very similar breed is the rare Loghtan, of which a few survive in the Isle of Man.

The two main types of British sheep are the mountain and the Down breeds. Of the former the Scotch Blackface and the Welsh Mountain are typical examples. All through the summer they range on mountain pastures, being rounded up by dogs for such essential purposes as dipping, branding and sorting for sale. The fat Downland sheep, such as the Hampshire Down and the Suffolk, live on lowland farms and have crops such as turnips and kale especially grown for them. Midway between them are grassland sheep, such as the Clun and Kerry Hill, which get their living mostly from grass and have become very popular because they are so adaptable.

Aberdeen Angus steer, a meat champion, owned by Sainsbury's

Highland cattle on Lord Lovat's estate at Glen Strath Farrar in Inverness-shire

The Dorset Horn, at home chiefly in West Dorset and East Somerset, is unusual in that it will produce three crops of lambs in two years. Whereas most lambs are born in spring, the Dorset Horn can be induced to produce lambs in autumn. Another horned breed, the Wiltshire Horn, has the peculiarity of growing hardly any wool. Oddly enough, this breed is now confined to an area of North-amptonshire and Buckingham-shire and to North Wales, instead of to Wiltshire. A hundred and fifty years ago there were half a million of them on Salisbury Plain, but breeders, in trying to improve them, so weakened the stock that they would not thrive on the bleak downs. So they were saved from extinction in a couple of regions where they are in favour for crossing, to produce early lambs.

Another breed, once common but now almost extinct, is the Cotswold. It produced the wool on which the wealth of England was established in medieval times and which provided the money for building those lovely Cotswold houses and churches. Now that sheep are kept primarily for meat rather than wool, the Cotswold is found to mature too slowly, and only one or two flocks remain.

Pigs too grunt away in their millions in British sties. Aboriginal pigs were black, white or ginger, or a mixture of the three. The only ginger (or 'foxy-red' as the breeders term it) breed to survive is the Tamworth, which is not very common. Recently a few Piétrain pigs, which are black, white and red, have been brought over from Belgium. An experiment to discover what type of pig would be produced by crossing a number of British breeds, all black and white, resulted in a black, white and red pig almost exactly similar to the Piétrain!

In 1953 a number of Landrace pigs were imported from Sweden and sold at fantastic prices. Since then this bacon breed has multiplied and forms an important proportion of our national herd. Landrace are long, low-bodied, white pigs with lop ears, in contrast to the other common breed, the Large White,

Jersey cow, named Four-Leaf Blondie, winner at Malvern Three Counties Show. Similar to the Guernsey, and both from the Channel Islands

which has prick ears. But certain of the rarer white breeds, such as the Cornish and Cumberland, also have lop ears, it being alleged, no doubt with malice, that the long ears prevent the pig from seeing its way to escape through holes in the dilapidated stone walls!

You will often see the Wessex

Galloway cow and calf. Mrs Murray Usher's three-year-old prizewinner from Scotland, but this beef breed is now widespread in England

and Essex Saddleback pigs, so-called because they have a white band, like a saddle, across their broad black backs. One of the less common breeds is the Gloucester Old Spot, which is a white pig sprinkled with black spots, something like a Dalmatian dog.

Man's oldest animal partner in farming is the horse, but it is now quite an event to see a heavy horse working on a farm. In East Anglia and the Fens they are still used for drawing heavy loads of sugar beet and vegetables from the fertile fields to the hard roads. These horses are most likely to be Suffolk Punches. They are magnificent chestnut horses, without fringes of hair (or 'feathers') around their hooves, and are probably descended from the horses bred in this part of the country by the Iceni in the time of Boadicea.

Scottish blackface sheep. These, by Loch Lomond, can feed on heather and do not need grass

The other breeds are the Shires, which are distinguished by heavy 'feathering', the Clydesdales, which are a Scottish breed resembling the Shires but usually coloured roan and white, and the Percherons. These last are white, or grey, horses, descended from those brought back from Northern France by soldiers in the First World War. They would have become very popular if tractors had not been invented, to make them redundant. Nowadays the best place to see fine horses is in the big towns, as, for instance, in London, where they are still used in brewers' drays, for old times' sake.

I shall have little to say about poultry. Not only do most of them

Hampshire Down lambs. There are over forty kinds of sheep in Britain and this one is immensely popular all over the world

Romney Marsh ram (before shearing). It has formed the basis of farming throughout the world and is the founder of New Zealand's flocks

now live in large, intensive units, out of sight of passers-by, but they do not belong to the old breeds any more. Hatching poultry is now in the hands of large firms which operate on an international basis. Each has its own synthetic breeds, built up from the old pure-breds according to secret formulae worked out by highly paid geneticists. Instead of a farmer now pointing to a resplendent cock scratching on a dunghill and saying 'That's a Dorking', he cautiously opens the door of a hangar-like building, reveals about ten thousand prating hens and says 'Those are 404s', which somehow seems not

nearly so romantic. Still, when we see a roadside sign advertising 'Eggs', it is worth while pulling up for a dozen from the old-time free-ranging breeds.

Let us turn to farm crops. One of the most significant developments in the past thirty years has been the recognition that grass is a crop and not something that just grows naturally out of doors. Farmers now sow carefully blended mixtures of grasses, which they call 'leys', for a predetermined number of years. Thus a one-year ley will be composed of different grasses and be given different treatment from a three-year ley. The important commercial grasses are four in number, namely, cocksfoot, timothy, rye-grass and meadow fescue, and they are usually mixed with red or white clover.

Britain, it is said, has the best climate in the world for growing crops and the worst for harvesting them. This is most frustrating, because the British farmer's great problem is to grow and preserve enough food in the five summer months to feed his livestock for the seven winter ones. Haymaking was

Landrace pigs, next to the Large White the commonest British breed. These were supreme at the Smithfield Show. Note the long sides for bacon

Wessex Saddleback pig. It grunts everywhere in England and formed the basis of the American Hampshires

always a tricky business, which is why the modern alternative of silage-making has become popular. Silage is grass preserved green (instead of being dried, as in hay) by pressing it to exclude air. Nevertheless much hay is still made, though it is now mostly bound into bales and then stacked. Some of it is dried artificially, by heated air circulated by fans.

Grass is not the only crop which can be used for silage. Kale and potatoes can be treated in the same way, and a year or two ago maize became quite popular. Maize is a spectacular crop, growing to a height of ten or twelve feet and looking like a plantation of sugar-cane. Not many of the cobs ripen in our climate, and the whole plant is chopped up for silage in the late autumn.

When silage-making first began to be popular in the late 1940's, most farmers collected the cut grass on buck-rakes, which are composed of a line of forks mounted on the back of a tractor. About 1958 the forage (or silage) harvester was introduced and is now to be found on almost every farm. It looks like a combination of

Suffolk mare and foals. This chestnut breed is very ancient and has claims to going back to Celtic times—now much improved by breeding

a lawn-mower and vacuum cleaner. Whirling blades slash through and chop up the grass, and the current of air created by their action forces the chewed-up material through a spout into a waiting trailer.

Silage may be stored in outdoor clamps, resembling chunks of cheese, or in covered clamps, usually with sides made of railway sleepers and with a roof overhead, or in specially erected metal towers. There are other methods. An amateur archaeologist not long ago thought he had discovered a range of unknown barrows, only to learn that they were circular silage clamps, made by excavating a hole, filling it with silage and covering it with chalk and earth!

Tractors, the maids-of-all-work on the farm. One is pulling a plough and the other is baling straw; but they do many, many jobs

Combine harvesters at work on a huge corn farm in the west country

Silage-making is only a part of modern grassland management. A ley, ideally, should be cut and grazed alternately. The electric fence is quite popular as a method for controlling grazing. It is worked from a battery and is moved once or twice a day, allowing the farmer to give his cattle a strip of grass exactly adequate for their needs. He calculates how much that is on paper beforehand. An alternative is to divide the pasture into a number of small paddocks, using each in turn for a few days. If you keep your eyes open you may see both systems in common use. After each use the grass field is given a dressing of chemical fertilizer.

At the end of the set period of years the ley is ploughed up. The field then grows corn crops for a few years, to cash in on the accumulated fertility.

Travelling through the countryside you will see fields of wheat, barley and oats. In some parts of the country you will find vast, rolling prairies of corn, of all shades from yellow to bronze in August. Nowadays these are nearly all of wheat and barley. Since horses, which fed on oats, have disappeared, few farmers grow oats, except in

Wales and Scotland. In the wet climate of those two countries they are often cut unripe and fed in winter to cattle, both straw and grain together.

Wheat is usually sown in autumn and barley in spring, though, to confuse the issue, there are autumn-sown varieties of barley and spring-sown varieties of wheat. To tell the difference between the stiff-strawed, stocky-headed wheat and the limp, prickly-awned barley is easy at harvest-time, but it is not so simple in spring. A useful clue is that, whereas wheat has a broad, blue-green blade, barley has a thinner leaf of paler green, with a twist in it. It looks as though it has had a permanent wave.

Both wheat and barley now yield much heavier crops than they did. Modern farmers often harvest more than two tons of grain per acre. One reason for the improvement is the success of agricultural scientists in breeding new and more prolific varieties of cereals. You will not be in conversation for long with a grain-growing farmer before you will hear him talking of *Proctor* barley and *Cappelle* wheat.

At sowing time the farmer uses an ingenious machine known as a combine-drill. This not only sows the corn in rows but deposits grains of blended fertilizer at the same time, for the plants to feed on as soon as they start growing. Before the actual sowing, other modern machines play their part in the fields. One of the newest is the rotary cultivator, or rotorator, which, by whirling blades powered by a tractor, pulverizes the soil and creates a fine seed-bed. Even the spreading of farmyard manure has now been mechanized, and machines throw muck merrily all round.

The basis of all modern work on the land is, of course, the tractor. Slow, old-fashioned machines with iron wheels first began to drive the horses off the farms between the two wars. At first they simply pulled adapted implements designed for use with horses, but now they have a whole range of implements of their own. Most modern tractors have a power-take-off to which geared machinery, such as rotary cultivators and forage-harvesters, can be attached. To the front of the tractor is attached a foreloader, which acts as a scoop or a lifting arm. Tractors range from very light, fast, mobile machines for transport work to huge, track-laying juggernauts which can pull ploughs up steep hillsides or uproot small trees.

After sowing, the chief operation on corn-growing farms before harvest is the spraying of the crops. Most farmers have a spraying tank and boom, mounted behind a tractor, with which they spray their corn with weed-killer in May. Large acreages are sometimes sprayed from the air, either by small aircraft or, perhaps more efficiently, by helicopter.

In August at harvest time some farmers, particularly in the north and west, still cut their corn with a binder, tie it in sheaves and then stack it in ricks, which are later threshed by a threshing-machine.

In the main grain-growing parts of the country, however, most corn is cut with a combine-harvester—a monster machine which crawls around the harvest field like a huge all-devouring beetle, easily picking up beaten-down and broken crops. Afterwards the baler will follow and produce neat cubes of straw for rick-making.

While ricks of corn are still to be seen it is fascinating to note the differences in traditional pattern in different districts. Scottish ricks are round and pointed, and most of them are very small, containing just enough corn to be threshed during a short winter day. East Anglian ricks are, or were, massive and boat-shaped, with parallel sides and rounded ends. Ricks in the south country were squat and chunky, but here and there, as in central Somerset, an area of round ricks probably indicated the existence of an island of farmers of Celtic descent in a region otherwise mainly Anglo-Saxon. It is well known that in architecture, as in other matters, the Celts preferred curves, while the unimaginative Anglo-Saxons preferred things to be uncompromisingly rectangular.

Ricks have to be thatched, and as the need for making ricks disappeared it was at one time feared that the thatcher's art would vanish. Happily our villages have been invaded by new residents who not only appreciate the picturesque artistry of thatch but can also afford to pay for it! The thatcher flourishes as never before, though now he spends his time on cottages rather than ricks. He will finish his work with a flourish, with straw peacocks, pheasants and even deer on the ridge. He is, however, short of thatching straw, which was once a plentiful by-product of harvest but which now comes out of the combine-harvester useless for the purpose. Wheat has either to be harvested by binder in the old-fashioned way, and threshed with a special machine which deals lightly with the straw, or else the thatcher has to use reed instead of wheat straw. Much reed is even having to be imported from the Continent.

A peep inside the barn of a big grain-growing farmer will reveal an enormous, complicated and very expensive battery of equipment for drying, conveying and storing the corn. On some farms the storage silos are cylindrical buildings erected out of doors. The very latest idea is to store the grain damp in glass-lined, metal silos that are hermetically sealed, and these can usually be identified by the fact that they are bright and shining and have rounded tops.

Although modern farm buildings, of which great numbers are being erected, are usually constructed of concrete and asbestos, many very old buildings have been cleverly adapted for modern use. In particular, in many parts of the country, medieval barns, such as the great monastic tithe barns, are still used for storing grain, often in modern bins. Where good building stone occurs the farmer still uses it freely. Even the old art of dry-stone walling, which means building field walls without mortar, has been revived.

Travelling about the country introduces us to many specialist areas. Kent, for example, abounds in fruit orchards and hop gardens, of which the old oast-houses, with their revolving cowls, are evidence. The Fens specialize in sugar beet and horticultural crops, such as carrots and celery, which can use their deep and fertile soils. In Herefordshire we find, as well as Hereford cattle, hops, orchards and blackcurrant plantations, the latter a recent innovation. In Lincolnshire there are miles of potatoes. Perthshire has large acreages of seed potatoes and raspberries, and Hampshire possesses valuable watercress beds. In the areas round London and big cities like Birmingham or Liverpool you will find market gardens growing salad and green crops for the city's food, especially in the river valleys with their deep silted loam. Here, as in the Lea Valley in Essex, Hertfordshire and at Worthing in Sussex, you will find much grown under glass. Indeed, every county and district has its own agricultural character distinct from anything to be found elsewhere; but on the high ground and the fertile plains the main crops will be wheat, oats and barley stretching for miles in fields of huge size.

10: The Country Code Says:

Guard Against All Risk of Fire

Fasten All Gates

Keep Dogs under Proper Control

Keep to the Paths across Farm Land

Avoid Damaging Fences, Hedges and Walls

Leave No Litter

Safeguard Water Supplies

Protect Wild Life, Wild Plants and Trees

Go Carefully on Country Roads

Respect the Life of the Countryside

The Country Code, in complete form, can be obtained from any bookshop or from Her Majesty's Stationery Office in Kingsway, London, W.C.2, price 6*d*. (or by post 8*d*.).

11: Societies You Should Know About

The National Trust. Full title is National Trust for Places of Historic Interest or Natural Beauty, 42 Queen Anne's Gate, London, S.W.1. Is a private voluntary body owning or keeping in trust some hundreds of treasures of building and land. Issues an Annual Report which can be had free.

The Ministry of Public Building and Works. Known shortly as the Ministry of Works. Owns about five hundred sites, mostly buildings and ancient monuments. Issues guides to most places. Season tickets are also issued giving cheap access to all properties. A list of its properties (price 1s. 6d.) can be obtained from Her Majesty's Stationery Office, York House, Kingsway, London, W.C.2.

The Forestry Commission. Owns, for the public, thousands of acres of forestry lands. Issues guides to many of its estates, including, for instance, the New Forest. A list of publications is obtainable from Her Majesty's Stationery Office, Kingsway, London, W.C.2, or from the Forestry Commission, 25 Savile Row, London, W.1.

The National Parks Commission. Exists to establish National Parks and Long Distance Footpaths and Bridle Paths in areas of special natural beauty. Also tries to protect areas of beauty from being spoiled by ugly development. Has already specified ten National Parks in areas as wide apart as the Peak and Lake Districts and Dartmoor, and Areas of Outstanding Natural Beauty in districts ranging from the Isle of Wight to the Solway Coast. Long Distance Routes have already been established in part in some areas, notably the Pennine Way, the South Downs Way and the Pembrokeshire Coast Path. Annual Report from Her Majesty's Stationery Office in Kingsway, London, W.C.2. Office: 1 Cambridge Gate, Regent's Park, London, N.W.1.

The Nature Conservancy. Selects and administers areas suitable for the conservation and control of the flora and fauna. Has 111 reserves from open downland to wildfowl stations and seal and fisheries protection. Also maintains Research Stations and makes international conservation agreements. Issues Annual Report from Her Majesty's Stationery Office, Kingsway, London, W.C.2. Offices: 19 Belgrave Square, London, S.W.1.

The Fauna Preservation Society, c/o The Zoo, Regent's Park, London N.W.1. Helps to protect rare mammals.

The Royal Society for the Protection of Birds. Has a special club for young people. Address: The Lodge, Sandy, Bedfordshire.

The World Wildlife Fund (2 Caxton Street, London, S.W.1). Runs a young people's branch, the Wildlife Rangers, and particulars may be had from 120 London Road, Morden, Surrey.

The Council for Nature. Represents all natural history societies in Britain and will give inquirers the address of their county or local natural history society. Office: 41 Queen's Gate, London, S.W.7.

Historic Churches Preservation Trust. Makes funds available for the preservation of ancient churches and issues cheap booklets. Details from Fulham Palace, London, S.W.6.

Society for the Protection of Ancient Buildings. Seeks to preserve irreplaceable old buildings of all kinds from churches and mansions to cottages. Office: 55 Great Ormond Street, London, W.C.1.

12: A Few Words about Maps

YOU must equip yourself with a few maps. The one-inch to the mile 'Popular' Ordnance Survey maps are essential guides to your own area and give masses of information. To get a close-up view of the place in which you live get one of the 2½-inch scale: they show almost every building, wood, pond, stream, church, guide-post and post office, and give distances to the nearest big town or city. They show whether a church has a spire or a tower and whether a wood is deciduous or evergreen! They also show ancient remains and footpaths, and these are generally in agreement with those fixed by the Footpaths Act. The Ordnance Survey maps of Regions (4 miles to 1 inch) are useful when you are car-travelling over a large area and across more than a county.

If you study maps you can, with practice, 'see' the look of the countryside before you get there, by watching chiefly the contour lines giving the heights of land along a particular line.

Learn the so-called conventional signs used on Ordnance Survey maps. By remembering what they mean you can often amaze your car driver by telling him, for instance, when he will come to a hill or a wood or a church, or whether he will go over or under the railway, or pass across an embankment or through a cutting. If you write to the Ordnance Survey, Chessington, Surrey, and ask for a Conventional Sign Card for the 1-inch map they will send you one free of charge.

If you carry a map and a cheap compass, and keep your eye on the position of the sun, you need never get lost. Better still, you can find your way anywhere.

13: The Popular Shell Books on the Countryside

THE SHELL COUNTRY BOOK, edited by Geoffrey Grigson, is a very complete guide, in extensive text and picture, to man and nature in the countryside. It contains 48 coloured plates.

THE SHELL NATURE BOOK is a magnificent colour guide to the flowers, trees, birds, beasts and the wild life of the country. Its special feature is the inclusion of 60 quarto full-page colour plates.

THE SHELL GARDENS BOOK, edited by Peter Hunt, is a survey of gardens and gardening in Britain. It contains a list of gardens open to the public, and is fully illustrated in colour and monochrome.

THE SHELL AND B.P. GUIDE TO BRITAIN, edited by Geoffrey Boumphrey, is a comprehensive guide to the sights of forty-eight British counties. It is fully illustrated in colour and monochrome.

THE SHELL COUNTY GUIDES, edited by John Betjeman and John Piper. Each guide offers a portrait of the county and a gazetteer of most cities, towns and villages.

These books, like this SHELL TREASURY OF THE COUNTRYSIDE, are obtainable from any bookshop.

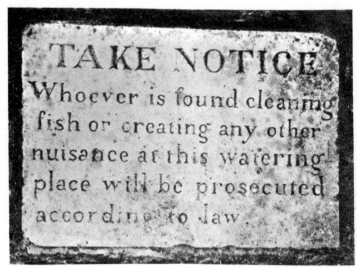